DATE DUE

UPI 261-2505   PRINTED IN U.S.A.

Albert Einstein and the Cosmic World Order

Albert Einstein and the Cosmic World Order

CORNELIUS LANCZOS

School of Theoretical Physics

Dublin Institute for Advanced Studies

Six Lectures Delivered
at The University of Michigan
in the Spring of 1962

INTERSCIENCE PUBLISHERS

a division of John Wiley & Sons, Inc.

New York · London · Sydney

Library of Congress Catalog Card Number: 65-12708
Printed in the United States of America

Preface

It is an encouraging symptom of our time—often decried as materialistic—that it chooses its heroes from individuals whose goals lie completely in the intellectual and spiritual sphere.

EINSTEIN (1921)

ALBERT EINSTEIN—the magic name of a scientist in the eyes of the layman, the prodigious physicist in the eyes of the professional—who was he? By invitation of Professor Robert Thrall of the Institute of Science and Technology at the University of Michigan in Ann Arbor, I had the privilege of elaborating on this theme in a public lecture series called "The Place of Albert Einstein in the History of Physics," delivered in the Spring of 1962 at the University of Michigan to a large gathering of faculty members, students, and educated laymen. The generous response of the audience encourages me to hope that the publication of these lectures in book form will receive an equally warm reception on the part of student and general reader alike.

The young student of physics today is doing his best to assimilate the heavy machinery of modern physics, which will enable him to write papers and become a respected member of the academic community. He has little time and inclination to speculate on the ultimate rationality of the cosmos and its possible implications for an integrated world picture. Such questions belong to the idle dreams of metaphysics but cannot concern the serious business of physics. Little does he realize that only a generation ago an idle dreamer lived among us, whose visions added a multitude of dimensions to our knowledge of the very small and the very large. In a world which went mad with aggression and murder, he listened to the cosmic melodies and jotted down harmonies of a boldness and power never heard before.

This book deals with the achievements of Albert Einstein, the greatest organ point of humanity in an era of noise and self-assurance, who restored the human intellect to its pedestal of dignity and humility.

I am indebted to Mr. Norman T. Burns, Head, Publication Service, Institute of Science and Technology, University of Michigan, for his painstaking editorial help.

CORNELIUS LANCZOS

Dublin, Ireland
October, 1964

Acknowledgments

THE AUTHOR expresses his thanks
to the Public Trustee and the Society of Authors, London, for permission to quote excerpts from the Shaw speech on pp. 113–115;
to Dr. O. Nathan, Trustee of the Einstein estate, for permission to quote brief passages from A. Einstein, *Ideas and Opinions* (Crown Publishers, New York, 1954); and
to Mr. Carl Seelig for permission to quote from his Einstein biography on pp. 7 and 127.

Appreciation and acknowledgment are expressed to the 1962 Class of the University of Michigan for establishing an Institute of Science and Technology Publishing Fund, which has aided in the publication of this work.

Ho, every one that thirsteth,
come ye to the waters,
and he that hath no money:
come ye, buy and eat;
yea, come, buy wine and milk
without money, and without price.

ISAIAH 55:1

Contents

1

The Greatness of Albert Einstein

The emotional state which leads to such achievements resembles that of the worshipper or the lover; the daily strive does not arise from a purpose or a programme, but from an immediate need.
  EINSTEIN addressing MAX PLANCK (1918)

SCIENCE HAS BECOME a household word in our days and in the bewildering variety of scientific discoveries we are sometimes apt to lose our bearings and feel the need for a solid resting point in contrast to the ephemeral restlessness of the contemporary scene. Somebody mentions the name Einstein and immediately our reaction is: "This is it. He is the man to whom we should turn."

But why? Why Einstein and not somebody else? Since the end of the last century a whole galaxy of great geniuses have appeared in physics: Here are Marie and Pierre Curie, the discoverers of radium. Here is Max Planck, the discoverer of a new radiation law which initiated an era of physics and became the basis of quantum theory. Here is Ernest Rutherford, who with his ingenious experiments demonstrated the commutability of chemical elements and at the same time paved the way toward a better understanding of the structure of the atom. Here is Niels Bohr, who created the theoretical edifice by which Rutherford's experiments became explainable. Here is Louis de Broglie, the discoverer of the strange "matter waves" which accompany the world of elementary particles. And finally here are the three

1

great founders of the modern theory of matter, called "wave mechanics," or "quantum mechanics": Heisenberg, Schroedinger, and Dirac.

Why then should we single out Einstein as *the* great physicist of our age?

Yet if we should have asked any one of these great physicists which man made the most fundamental contribution to the physics of the twentieth century, they would have answered without hesitation: Albert Einstein. The overwhelming importance of Einstein's physical discoveries and his unique place in the history of science is universally recognized and can hardly be contested. Nobody intends to diminish the merits of other great men of science, but there was something in Einstein's mental make-up which distinguished him as a personality without peers. He wrote his name in the annals of science with indelible ink which will not fade as long as men live on earth. There is a finality about his discoveries which cannot be shaken. Theories come, theories go. Einstein did more than formulate theories. He listened with supreme devotion to the silent voices of the universe and wrote down their message with unfailing certainty.

What was so astonishing in his manner of thinking was that he could discover the underlying principle of a physical situation, undeceived by the details, and penetrate straight down to the very core of the problem. Thus he was never deceived by appearances and his findings had to be acknowledged as irrefutable.

What can the educated layman grasp of the phenomenon Einstein? Is it possible that such a deep thinker can be understood only by his technically trained colleagues while the great bulk of humanity is left out in the cold? Is it true that the technical difficulties of the subject are so overwhelming that his findings cannot be put in a language understandable to the large group of people who have a good general education, although they have not been specifically trained in the exact sciences?

It is improbable that the findings of such a deep thinker could not be translated into a universally comprehensible language without losing too much of their substance. This is corroborated by the further circumstance that Einstein was never too much attracted to his technically trained colleagues, who spoke outwardly the same language but had a widely different approach to the deeper exploration of the mysteries of the universe. He considered himself more a philosopher than a professional physicist; he was more at home with visionary people—artists, writers, poets, actors—than with many of his professional associates. They followed the well-trodden path, laid out by the well-established rules of the game. Einstein never played the game according to the traditional rules. To him the universe was important and not the game we play with the universe. This distinction separated him from most of his contemporaries, to whom science is an occupation and not a religion of highest devotion and abandonment.

If we mention the name Einstein anywhere in the world, the response is unmitigated reverence and admiration. "Yes, Einstein, of course, the great physicist and mathematician." But then we ask the question: What do you know of him? What made this Einstein a world figure of such incomparable dimensions that he was held in mystical awe by millions of people as the revered voice of the universe? The answer is usually: "That I cannot tell you. You know, I was never too good in mathematics and to study Einstein you require so much higher mathematics that I am, of course, lost if it comes to really understanding what he has accomplished. I only know that he discovered something very important and that the name of this discovery is relativity."

This answer certainly seems reasonable enough, yet there is a flaw in it. Of course it is impossible to describe in a few sentences what such a great genius accomplished in a long life of ceaseless and devoted meditation. But by spending several hours in serious effort, it is by no means impossible to gain a fairly adequate concept of his achievements. There is so much in the line of general ideas in his investigations which can be stated without any (or with a minimum of) mathematical symbols that one can go a long way in pointing out the specific nature of his reasoning, without being hampered by the technicalities of the mathematical language. This is exactly what the following discussions attempt to do. We shall concentrate on a few fundamental ideas and try to elucidate them from many angles rather than get lost in a multitude of subjects. By this approach something of the scope of Einstein as a physicist will undoubtedly be lost. Einstein was not merely the creator of the theory of relativity. He discovered a host of other basic results in theoretical physics * and it has been pointed out more than once that if somebody asked: "Who is the greatest modern physicist after Einstein?" the answer would be: Einstein again. And why? Because, although the theory of relativity in itself would have established his fame forever, had somebody else discovered relativity, his other discoveries would still make him the second greatest physicist of his time.

Nevertheless, it is not an accident that in the popular mind his fame rests on the theory of relativity. His other discoveries could have been made by others. Moreover, they are discoveries which may be modified as science progresses. The theory of relativity, however, was an astonishing discovery which opened an entirely new door in our understanding of the physical universe and it is a door which will never be shut again. Our concepts of space and time have been radically changed by Einstein's first formulation of the principle of relativity, now called "special relativity." This happened when Einstein was only twenty-six years of age. But our most fundamental physical concepts, involving space, time, *and matter*, have been even more radically altered by Einstein's second formulation of the principle of relativity, called "general relativity," which came to its fruition ten years later, during the years 1915–16. Now not only space and time, but *space, time* and *matter* were amalgamated into one fundamental and inseparable unity. His discovery of this unity had a tremendous impact on Einstein's scientific philosophy. From now on he lost interest in the bewildering variety of physical phenomena and focused on one theme only: to find the unifying law which is the basis of all physical events. In the eyes of his colleagues he changed from a "physicist" to a "metaphysicist," a man out for the ultimates—and why should a scientist care for the ultimates?

To Einstein himself it made little difference by what label he

---

* Cf. the Epilogue.

was called. For him the watertight compartments in which we customarily classify our intellectual endeavors did not exist. As a true disciple of Kepler, he too listened to the secret music of the celestial spheres. Is that mathematics, or physics, or alchemy, or astronomy, or philosophy—what does it matter? To his colleagues the difference was that, whereas before he tackled —and how successfully!—all kinds of physical phenomena, now he shut himself up in the half-shadow of his study-room and lost touch with the contemporary problems of science.

Let us examine the phenomenon Einstein at closer range by discussing briefly his astonishing scientific career. He appeared on the scene in 1905, when he had barely finished his university studies. That year saw the appearance of three papers, each one of trailblazing magnitude and each one important for different reasons. The first one, on the so-called "Brownian motion" (named after an English botanist who first observed the phenomenon), dealt with a peculiar phenomenon which is observable in a highly magnifying microscope if we look carefully at an emulsion composed of little particles suspended in a fluid. We observe that these particles do not stand still but make peculiar jerky motions, a kind of dance which becomes the livelier the higher the temperature. If we follow the path of such a particle, we find a highly irregular zig-zag line, apparently without any inner law, as if it were a random phenomenon. Einstein showed that these jerky motions are caused by the many pushes that the suspended particle receives from the still smaller molecules of the fluid which collide with it. It is as if a big punching bag were suspended in the middle of the room and people from all sides were trying their skill on it. That such an apparently random phenomenon should actually satisfy a very definite mathematical law, which can be verified by observations, was surprising to the highest degree. It demonstrated the uncanny ability of Einstein in the line of statistical thinking which accompanied him throughout life and which is little known by those physicists and mathematicians who studied Einstein primarily for his relativistic discoveries.

It now seems hard to believe and yet is a fact that about sixty years ago many people doubted the existence of atoms. Today the atom is public property and the concept of atomic energy a household item in every educated person's thinking. In 1905 one still had the right to assume that the entire atomistic hypothesis was not more than a fake, invented solely to mystify and confuse the minds of physicists. Einstein's paper on the Brownian motion demonstrated almost palpably the correctness of the atomistic hypothesis and many scientists (among them the great physico-chemist Wilhelm Ostwald) who before had been on the doubting side were converted to atomism.

The second paper of 1905 dealt with the ideas of space and time and demonstrated that our common notions concerning the existence of an absolute space and an absolute time had to give way to a more flexible approach in which various observers have their own time measurements which do not agree with those of other observers. Few people understood the implications of this profound paper which was destined to play such a fundamental role in the later development of theoretical physics.

The third paper of Einstein also showed a remarkable maturity of scientific thinking. Planck deduced his famous radiation formula in 1900 by assuming that somehow energy is not emitted continuously but in small little packages, called "quanta," thus giving rise to the famous "quantum hypothesis." Einstein showed that Planck's demonstration of his law was in fact inconsistent and required a much more radical change of our concepts than the assumption of a discontinuous emission of energy. We have to assume that light is emitted and absorbed like a localized particle which travels from one point to another as a complete entity. For a hundred years we had learned that light is a wave phenomenon which spreads out on an ever-increasing sphere. To assume now that this was wrong, that light behaves in certain respects like a particle which remains concentrated in a very small volume as it travels from A to B instead of spreading out like a wave, was a strange conclusion indeed, but Einstein demonstrated the soundness and inevitability of such an assumption. This peculiar behavior of radiation, to be a wave from a certain point of view and yet a particle from another, has remained a puzzling mystery of physics up to our day. The first clear-cut formulation of this peculiar dualism—wave on the one side, particle on the other—goes back to Einstein's paper of 1905.

These papers were written in a peculiar style, very characteristic of Einstein's manner of thinking. They did not contain a great deal of mathematical formalism. There was a great deal of text and little in the line of formal manipulations. In the end the startling conclusion was there, obtained apparently with the greatest of ease, and by a reasoning which could not be refuted. Outside sources were hardly ever quoted; it looked as if the author had arrived at his results practically unaided, as if he had conjured up the whole procedure out of thin air, by a wave of his magic wand. This made Einstein suspicious in the eyes of his colleagues. A man who writes so clearly and with so few technicalities cannot be taken too seriously. Something must be wrong with him. It is not proper that he should deduce important results so elegantly, apparently without laborious efforts, and without consulting the opinions of others. And thus it happened that the majority of physicists ignored his work, while a few first-class minds, particularly Planck, Rubens, Nernst, and von Laue, accepted this amazing fledgeling as a full-grown member of their august community, in spite of the fact that he was much younger.

It is thus understandable that as early as 1909 Einstein received a call to a professorship at the University of Zürich. At that time he was employed as a minor consultant at the Swiss Patent Office in Berne. When he announced his resignation because he was going to Zürich as a professor of the university, his boss got red in the face and blurted out: "Now, Mr. Einstein, don't make any silly jokes. Nobody would believe such an absurdity." * Yet the absurdity was true, as were so many of the apparent "absurdities" which were encountered in Einstein's theories, and Einstein's fame spread more and more. In 1914 he was called to Berlin as director of the Physics Section of the world-famous Kaiser-Wilhelm-Institut, the highest honor that Germany could bestow on him. In the meantime he pursued his studies concerning the nature of radiation. These profound researches contributed fundamentally toward the development of quantum theory and the deeper understanding of the structure of the atom.

* Cf. Carl Seelig: *Albert Einstein* (Europa Verlag, Zürich, 1954), p. 108 (author's translation).

Between the years 1905 and 1925 he was the undisputed leader of a whole generation of theoretical physicists. Nobody could compete with him in the depth of comprehension and the uncanny simplicity with which he could derive fundamental results from a few basic experimental results.

In the meantime he was in the grip of a mighty idea which germinated slowly. Almost from the beginning he realized that his space-time theory of 1905 could not be considered as the final solution but only as a first step to something much more comprehensive. After ten years of incessant ponderings which led him to many false leads and cul-de-sacs, he arrived at his "general theory of relativity," which was hailed as his masterpiece and which Einstein himself considered as his most fundamental discovery. This theory showed that our customary ideas concerning geometry do not correspond to the geometry actually realized in the physical universe. The geometry which we have learned in school for thousands of years—it is called "Euclidean geometry," because it was the Greek geometer Euclid who put this geometry in a remarkably exact, scientific system—is in fact *not* the geometry of nature. It is true that Einstein's paper of 1905 had already demonstrated that our traditional ideas about space and time fall down if motions of high velocities are involved. But the mathematician Minkowski succeeded in translating Einstein's physical ideas into the language of geometry by showing that Einstein's theory can be interpreted as a new geometrical theory of the universe in which *space and time together* have to be considered as the proper subject of geometry, and not space alone. In other words, for the physical universe our ordinary space is only part of the picture; the full picture emerges if we add time to space and unify space and time into a world of not three but four dimensions. This new world was still of the Euclidean type; the difference was only that in our ordinary geometrical constructions we stop too soon. We start with a point, which has no extension, then follows a line which extends in length only, then a plane, which extends in length and width, then a space which extends in length, width, and height. Here we usually stop. But, Minkowski argued, we should not stop but go one step further by adding to length, width, and height one further dimension. This is the dimension of *time* which to our senses appears in such completely different garb, so completely incompatible with space, and yet it so happens that for the physical universe it plays exactly the role of an added dimension in a world which is formed out of *space and time*. Minkowski's view did not fundamentally alter our customary Euclidean geometry; it merely added one more dimension to it.

The new discovery of 1915 modified this picture very decisively by showing that the geometry of Euclid, even if extended from three to four dimensions, does not do full justice to the physical world because it pictures it geometrically in the form of a completely *flat* country. In actual fact we should imagine the universe as a *hilly* country with mountains and valleys, instead of as a monotonous plane which extends from infinity to infinity, free of any imperfections. Let us imagine bumps on this plane, like mole-hills which cover a field infested by rodents. What are these mole-hills? They appear to us as *matter*. Whenever we perceive matter at some place in the universe, we actually perceive a mole-hill on a generally flat field. These mole-hills were left out in Euclid's geometry but in fact they are the most important agents of the universe, since anything that happens in the universe is somehow related to the action of matter.

This theory was of tremendous abstraction and tremendous boldness. Never has the human mind perceived such astonishing constructions. We knew, of course, that geometry is important. We all learn geometry in school, even if later we forget almost everything of this truly fascinating subject. And why do we learn geometry? Because it is recognized that the laws of space are important, because, after all, it is this space in which physical action takes place. But notice the extraordinary change which came to our geometrical thinking through the meditations of a single man: Albert Einstein. In Newton's physics we had an empty space like a huge empty box, into which matter is put from the outside. In addition, we had time in which physical action takes place. We thus had three basic entities which were apparently completely independent of each other: space, time, and matter. But Minkowski's interpretation of Einstein's theory of special relativity showed that space and time are not independent of each other but form one inseparable unit, the world of space-time. This four-dimensional space-time world now took over the role of Newton's empty receptacle into which matter was put from the outside.

Then came Einstein's great discovery of 1915 which carried the synthesis to the ultimate. Matter is not put from the outside into an empty box but forms an integral part of geometry. Matter belongs to geometry. What we observe as matter is in fact a hill in a generally flat country. We can measure such a hill by its curvature. Curvature is a strictly geometrical quantity which apparently has nothing to do with physics. For example, we can measure the curvature of our globe by determining the radius of the earth, which is about 4000 miles. Now, if we put a certain amount of matter, such as a lump of steel, on a balance and found that it weighs, let us say, a pound, we would certainly not think that this pound has anything to do with a length. But Einstein's theory has shown that this pound can be converted into length because we can figure out the exact amount by which the generally flat Euclidean world has been indented by the presence of that pound of steel.

But then if time is nothing but length, and mass is nothing but length, what else do we have in physics? Space, time, matter—these are the three basic entities of the physical universe. Time has been absorbed by space as an added dimension. Matter has been absorbed by space as a curvature property of space. What is left? Is it possible that space is everything? Is it possible that if only we understood the proper geometry of space, we would understand *all* physics, since the whole physical universe is nothing but the manifestation of a certain kind of geometry?

This was an intoxicating thought which caught Einstein and never let him go again. Up to the discovery of general relativity he was a sober physicist like anybody else. He accepted the customary rules laid down by the empiricists. After all, what is the role of the theoretical physicist? He follows the lead of the experimental physicist. The experimental physicist finds certain relations on the basis of his measurements. Then comes the theoretical physicist who finds the mathematical equation which fits the measurements. If he is lucky, he may find a rather comprehensive mathematical equation which will fit many particular experiments. But can he ask the question: why did nature realize this particular equation and not something else? To ask such a question is not becoming to a physicist. He takes the results of observations for granted and if he succeeds with a precise mathematical description of the phenomena, his task as a physicist is ended. Thus, for example, Newton took the astronomical measurements of Kepler and found his famous gravitational theory, by which he could give a perfect description of planetary motion, in harmony with the observed facts. The only assumption he had to make was that between any two masses a force is acting which is proportional to the product of the masses and inversely proportional to the square of their distance. We may be inclined to ask, why the square of the distance and not the cube or some other power? But all such questions are idle because they go beyond the realm of observable facts. The observations verify the law of Newton, and that is enough. What else could happen if the observations were different is a nonsensical question since no such observations exist and we cannot go outside the world of facts which is given to us.

But the amazing thing about Einstein's discovery was that he did not follow the usual sequence. His theory was not motivated by some new gravitational experiments. He started on essentially *speculative* grounds, although on the firm basis of some well-known experimental facts whose correctness could not be doubted. He felt that these facts expressed more than some accidental relations, that in fact they were the emanation of some basic *principles* realized in the physical world. From here, by higher and higher abstractions and by making use of the most advanced tools of mathematics, he came to the formulation of certain equations, the celebrated "Einstein gravitational equations." In the case of Newton it was not so surprising that he arrived at the right law of gravity. He had the observations of Kepler at his disposal and by careful analysis of these observations he established a set of equations which described these observations perfectly. This was in his own time a very great achievement and nobody wants to tarnish to the slightest degree the ingenuity of Newton. The inverse square law of the gravitational force was demanded in order to account for the ellipses in which the planets revolve around the sun, according to the careful observations of Kepler.

Einstein's starting point was completely different. It had something to do with the general properties of space and time and the nature of reference systems which we erect for the purpose of physical measurements. From these very general speculations he suddenly arrived with logical necessity at his equations. This was not according to the established rules of the game. This was black magic more than anything else. To stare in empty air and pull out results from nothing as a result of speculations, as the old Greek philosophers were wont to do, was disdained since the time of Galileo as a nonsensical procedure. One had to experiment first and see what happened. Then one tried to codify these experiments by a mathematical equation. This had been the well-established rule for hundreds of years. And now Einstein dared to challenge this procedure by reverting to the dreams of the ancients who tried to *understand* nature on the basis of logical deductions rather than *describe* it on the basis of carefully conducted experiments. The magical thing about Einstein was, however, that he succeeded where the ancients failed. He had the mighty tools of mathematics at his disposal, developed in a slow evolution of more than two thousand years since the time of Plato and Aristotle. The equations of Einstein, arrived at by purely speculative means, told us that indeed the planets *had* to move around the sun in ellipses and not in something else because our universe is not any mathematical universe, but a marvelously *reasonable* and well-ordered mathematical universe, pervaded by a supreme Cosmic Wisdom.

Not only did the entire Newtonian theory fall out of the bag, but there were a few exceedingly delicate additional effects, not predicted by the Newtonian theory, which could be checked by very careful measurements. One of them involved the bending of light rays by the sun, which demanded a total eclipse of the sun for its verification. It was shortly after the First World War, in 1919, that an expedition organized by some English astronomers was able to check Einstein's prediction. The observations agreed perfectly with the prediction of the theory and it was now that Einstein became world-famous.

But Einstein was not a man who could rest on his laurels. He was too much wedded to the universe to care too much for human recognition. The psychological impact of the success of his theory was quite profound on Einstein himself, because it had shown him that inspired mathematical speculation can soar into heights that mere experimentation could never achieve. The idea that we may not merely *describe* the physical universe but *understand* its inner workings had an intoxicating effect on his thinking. If it was possible to achieve such a speculative victory in the field of gravitation, why should we stop here? Why should we not go further and try to find a similarly reasonable explanation for the other fundamental phenomena of nature, namely, electricity and the mysterious quantum effects? From 1925 on his interest in the current affairs of physics begins to slacken. He voluntarily abdicated his leadership as the foremost physicist of his time, and receded more and more into voluntary exile from the laboratory, a state into which only a few of his colleagues were willing to follow. During the last thirty years of his life he became more and more a recluse who lost touch with the contemporary development of physics. His eyes were glued on the universe and the possibility of penetrating to the ultimate core where all secrets would be resolved and understood as the emanation of a single world law. In his great paper of 1916 he showed how the replacement of Euclidean geometry by the more advanced geometry developed by the great German mathematician Riemann—and thus called Riemannian geometry—was able to explain all the gravitational phenomena. But electricity did not seem to find its natural place in this geometry and thus he attempted to give it up in favor of a still more comprehensive form of geometry. Again and again he jubilantly felt that he had found the final answer, but again and again he admitted his defeat, returning to his starting point. In the last ten years of his life he settled for a certain "unified field theory" which he considered the final answer and the true fulfillment of all his hopes. Yet we have good reasons to doubt that he truly achieved his goal.

Nor is this point of any importance in the evaluation of Ein-

stein as a man and a scientist. He has given us a new picture of
the universe and he has demonstrated the power of inspired abstract thinking. Never before had any human being attained
such marvelous insights into the inner heart of the physical universe. Never before would it have been possible even to hope
that some day our minds may clearly recognize the master plan
according to which the universe is constructed. What he accomplished in a single lifetime is stupendous and a sufficient basis for
research for hundreds of years to come. In an era of unprecedented aggressiveness and destruction he held up a mirror to the
human mind which demonstrated its greatness and its boundless
possibilities if turned toward inspired constructive reasoning. He
thus occupies a place in the history of civilization which is unique
and may never be duplicated.

DISCUSSION

QUESTION. What was Einstein's relation to mathematics?

ANSWER. Einstein's attitude toward mathematics went through a
considerable change during his life. In the early years of his scientific career he was under the influence of the Viennese philosopher and physicist Ernst Mach and consequently displayed a
rather sceptical view toward mathematics. Mach was wedded to
the view that anything that could be interpreted as "metaphysical"
or "absolute" should be expurgated from the domain of science.
Hence he was anxious to show that mathematics could not be considered in any way as an absolute necessity in physical research.
In his view it was a purely historical accident that the mathematical
sciences became so predominant after the Renaissance; under different cultural influences physics could have taken a completely different turn. The early Einstein shared with Mach a certain suspicion
of mathematics. He was afraid that the elegance of the mathematical mechanism might obscure the physical problem and give a
purely formalistic answer which might smother the deeper essence
of the physical situation.

This attitude changed radically with the advent of general
relativity. In his search for the general solution of the problem
of coordinates he soon realized that without the heavy mechanism
of absolute calculus (also called "tensor calculus") no progress of
any kind would be conceivable. He soon saw that here was an
apparently brittle and uninspiring chapter of mathematics that

could be molded into something eminently lively and physical. From then on his predilection for mathematical constructions never left him because he realized that the future progress of theoretical physics would lean more and more on strictly mathematical models which cannot be interpreted in so-called "physical" terms. In fact, in his later years he was occasionally deceived by purely formal analogies which he invoked for the explanation of physical phenomena although they did not possess that clarifying and persuasive feature that the theory of tensors and Riemannian geometry possessed to such a high degree.

QUESTION. Is it not true that special relativity, that is, Einstein's theory of 1905, had a much greater and more lasting effect on physics than his general relativity theory of 1915?

ANSWER. This is true and under the circumstances easily understandable. Special relativity established the unity of space and time and gave a very definite prescription by which all the previous equations of physics had to be modified in order to harmonize with this new geometrical model of the universe which demanded that time should not play a role independent of space. Special relativity thus had repercussions in all branches of physics. General relativity, although of much more fundamental character, is first of all restricted to the phenomenon of universal gravitation, which is a relatively well-investigated chapter of physics in no way comparable in importance to the electric and quantum phenomena. Moreover, up to now general relativity could give no clues concerning the atomistic structure of matter and was thus of no help in the understanding of nuclear phenomena. There is little doubt that in a future, more comprehensive theory of matter Einstein's general relativity will play a leading and decisive role.

2

The Problem
of Reference Systems

*The application of algebra to geometry has, far more than any
of his metaphysical speculations, immortalized the name of
Descartes, and constitutes the greatest single step ever made in
the progress of the exact sciences.*
JOHN STUART MILL (1878)

WE TAKE our starting point from a remarkable idea which the
great Dutch physicist, Christian Huygens, developed around 1668
(about twenty years before the appearance of Newton's celebrated "Principia"). In the early days of the science of mechanics the problem of *collision* was one of the foremost topics
of discussion. What happens if two balls, coming from different
directions with different velocities, collide? How will they continue their motion? The game of billiards was already well
known, but one would have liked to understand the problem of
collision from a theoretical point of view. The full theory of the
motions of the billiard ball is very complicated because the balls
not only move in a straight line but also spin around their axes.
Furthermore, in a realistic appraisal the friction between ball and
table has also to be taken into account. These complications
could not be properly calculated, of course, in those days. One
was satisfied with the simplest case of collision in which two balls

collide *centrally* with each other. How will they continue their motion after the collision?

It was clear from the beginning that the *masses* of the balls are of vital importance. A very heavy and a very light ball will obviously behave quite differently if a collision takes place. But even the collision of two *equal* masses seemed interesting enough. It was known from experience that if a moving ball hits a ball of equal mass which is at rest, they exchange their state of motion: the ball *A* which has hit the ball *B* comes to rest, while the ball *B* moves away with the same velocity that the ball *A* had before hitting *B*.

Now Huygens had a very ingenious way of explaining this phenomenon and generalizing it to the case in which two balls of equal masses but arbitrary states of motion collide with each other. Huygens argued as follows. Let us assume that it is not ourselves who make the observation but another observer *O*. He put this imaginary observer *O* halfway between the balls. We see from Figure 1 that *O* is in motion relative to us. In fact, we see from the geometry of our problem that the observer *O* moves relative to us in a straight line, with constant velocity.

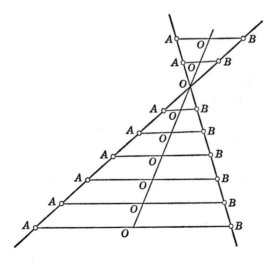

Figure 1

What does the observer O see? He sees two balls coming toward him with equal velocities, the ball A coming from the left, the ball B from the right. Now Huygens makes use of the principle of *symmetry*. He says that there is no preference in space for left or right. The two balls have the same mass and both of them move equally, except for the directions of left and right. The one is the perfect mirror image of the other. Hence it is unthinkable that after the collision one should be in any way preferred to the other. This means that, as viewed by the observer O, both balls must separate with equal velocities. The question now is, how does this velocity compare with the original velocity? Can the new velocity be *larger* than the original velocity? This possibility can be excluded at once. We know that a moving body can do work; it represents a certain amount of *energy*. Had the velocity been increased after the collision, this would mean that energy had been created out of nothing, which is impossible. On the other hand, assuming that the new velocity is less than the original velocity, we would have *lost* energy and that is certainly possible if a certain amount of energy is dissipated in the form of heat. But assuming that our balls are *elastic*, we know that an elastic collision involves very little heat loss. Hence in the case of an elastic collision we can conclude that the two balls separate with the same velocity with which they were endowed before the collision.

Now we translate the observation of O into our own world. Then we find by the laws of geometry that we can formulate the law of the elastic collision of two equal balls as follows. The ball A takes over the velocity of the ball B in both magnitude and direction, while the ball B takes over the velocity of the ball A in both magnitude and direction. Or expressed in still briefer form: the two balls simply exchange their state of motion.

What is remarkable in this derivation of Huygens is that a physical result is obtained on essentially *speculative* grounds. The principle of left-right symmetry expresses a very general universal property of our space. The principle of the conservation of energy is certainly of an empirical nature but once again it represents an all-comprehensive principle of fundamental significance.

The manner in which Einstein obtained his results is very similar in character. He had a remarkable ability to detect the fundamental elements in every physical situation. While other physicists struggled with the details and never arrived at the real substance of the problem, he said: "Our observations demonstrate the validity of the following general principle." Hence he never dealt with specific *equations* but with all-comprehensive *principles* from which profound consequences could be deduced.

But Huygens' reasoning is particularly interesting from still another angle. He employs here in his proof for the first time that "principle of relativity" which in Einstein's hands attained such fundamental importance. He engages a *second observer*, who is in a different state of motion from our own. We are at rest, he is in motion. Or looking at it from his standpoint: he is at rest and we are in motion. It then becomes necessary to *translate* his observations into our world. We drew conclusions with respect to the observer *O*. But is it so self-evident that we can translate his findings into our world? Obviously, we have to be careful. His statement: "I see a ball coming from the left and another coming from the right with equal speeds" is certainly true in his system. It is not true, however, in our system.

Huygens' reasoning brings thus into evidence a point of great importance. The same physical phenomenon may be observed by various observers. Each one of these observers lives in his own world and makes his own measurements. It is our task to *correlate* the findings of the various observers. It is important to find out how our own observations will appear to another observer, and vice versa. If we failed to do so, we could not tell how much of a given physical observation belongs to the objective physical world and how much to the accidental circumstances of the observer. Hence our task is to get definite information concerning the problem of how *we* would judge the observations of an observer who is in a different physical state from our own, and vice versa. Curiously enough, this question was never thoroughly investigated before Einstein brought it into focus. In other fields of endeavor the problem was well known. In psychology, for example, we say that a person may *project* himself into the mental state of another person. A great actor can identify himself with a different person and play his role as if he were that person himself. In physics a somewhat different terminology is used. First of all we employ the expression "reference system," which is an eminently descriptive and useful expression. Every observer has his own "reference system"; that is, he makes measurements with respect to certain basic orientations which belong specifically to him and have no universal validity.

In recent years—perhaps under the impact of the great importance of relativistic ideas—the same word became popular in many fields which lie outside the realm of physics. Thus we might say, for example, that an economist uses capitalism as his basic frame of reference, or perhaps Marxism, or socialism. In literature various literary styles, belonging to the classical, or romantic, or realistic period, establish various frames of reference. The same holds for various systems of religion (Christianity, Buddhism, Pantheism), or philosophy (positivism, idealism, Kantianism), and many other activities of the human mind. The fundamental fact holds in all these endeavors that *we must be anchored somewhere.* We cannot be suspended in thin air, we must have a platform under our feet. And even if one is suspended in thin air, as, for example, an astronaut in orbit, who is in a weightless and completely disoriented state, he can still use his capsule as a basic frame of reference.

Now in physics this question concerning a "frame of reference" arises specifically in connection with *measurements.* To measure means to associate a definite number with a certain physical quantity. For example, we may measure the mass of a body. For this purpose we need first of all a definite *unit,* let us say a "gram." Then the problem of measuring a mass is solved by putting the unknown mass on one scale of the balance and so many grams on the other. But there are other situations. Let us suppose we have to measure the position of a planet in astronomy. This cannot be done in such a simple manner as measuring a mass on a balance. We need certain fixed points in the universe. But where are these fixed points? No matter what we may choose as "fixed points," we cannot help operating with certain entities which have no absolute significance. There are no natural landmarks in space and thus we are forced to set up some artificial landmarks. But then we have to be aware of the fact that these landmarks were set up *by ourselves*. They do not have absolute qualities within the frame of the physical universe.

How do we orient ourselves in a city? In many cities of the United States there is an east-west division line and a north-south division line, with streets running parallel to the one division line and streets (sometimes for the sake of distinction called "avenues") running parallel to the other division line (Figure 2). We have First, Second, Third, etc., Streets running in the east-west direction and again First, Second, Third, etc., Streets (or perhaps avenues) running in the north-south direction. Hence we may have an address such as 600 N. 400 W., which would mean the intersection of the sixth avenue to the north (running in the north-south direction) with the fourth street to the west (running

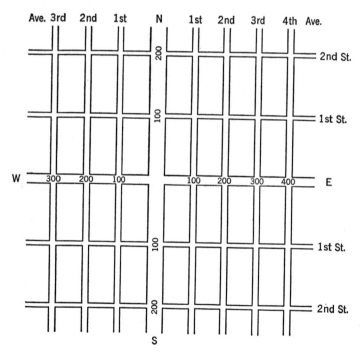

Figure 2

can arrive at all our geometrical conclusions without drawing the figures, solely on the basis of algebra, operating with the three "coordinates" x, y, z (or in plane geometry the two coordinates x and y). Even a blind person can pursue geometry if he has studied mathematics. He can derive all the properties of figures, although he is unable to visualize them. This is the power of the abstract analytical method, which takes the place of the direct visual construction.

Newton wholeheartedly accepted the method of Descartes for the purpose of physical deductions, and in fact we would not be able to formulate the laws of physics in mathematical form without the Cartesian method of introducing a definite rectangular reference system by which we orient ourselves in space.

The concept of coordinates is remarkably simple. The student of analytical geometry becomes acquainted with it in the very first hour of his course and immediately proceeds to apply the method to a variety of specific problems. And yet there are some very fundamental questions involved in this construction which deserve attention and which had never been fully discussed until the arrival of Einstein. Once Einstein was asked how it had happened that he and not somebody else had discovered relativity. He answered that he considered the following circumstance as decisive. Most people come in touch with the problems of space in their early youth, and when they are mature they no longer ask any questions. He, however, came in touch with the problems of space in his adult years and thus he saw problems which had been overlooked by others because of their apparent triviality. Indeed, although coordinates were used in physics for hundreds of years, nobody approached the problem from the fundamental viewpoint that characterized Einstein's approach.

The problem is this. We have the right to set up coordinate axes with the help of which we can orient ourselves in space. We establish a Cartesian frame of axes or a "Cartesian reference system." But there is an infinite variety of such systems. We cannot find an absolute center in space, nor are there preferential directions in space which would decide for us how we should orient our coordinate axes. We can set up an infinite variety of coordinate systems by putting the center of the reference system at any point of space and orienting our coordinate axes in any way we like, although keeping them mutually orthogonal. This means that the same physical event can be viewed from an infinity of reference systems, all of them being equally suited to the task of serving as a possible framework for our physical measurements.

This feature of a reference system is often masked by some specific features of the geometrical situation. For example, in studying the geometrical properties of an ellipse we immediately set up our coordinate axes in such manner that they coincide with the major and the minor axes of the ellipse (Figure 5). This is very natural since it greatly simplifies our calculations if the orientation of the coordinate axes harmonizes with the symmetry structure of the figure we want to study. But it would be a mistake to believe that this procedure is dictated by absolute necessity. Except for an increased complication of our formulae, we would not go wrong if we oriented our axes in any other manner we like.

Now if it is true that we can describe the same physical situation by an infinity of reference systems, it becomes imperative to correlate to each other the infinite variety of measurements

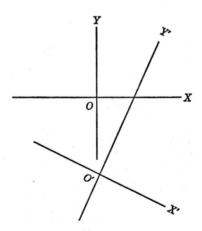

Figure 5

Figure 6

made by all the observers who are attached to this bewildering variety of equally legitimate reference systems.

That this is by no means an idle question can easily be seen. Suppose we are inside an airplane which is flying perfectly level. The force of gravity is directed downward (Figure 6) and we can walk back and forth on the floor of the cabin without any effort; in fact, if the flight is perfectly smooth, we shall not feel in the least that we are in motion. But let us now assume that the plane is in a climb (Figure 7). Then walking on the floor toward the front of the aircraft is much more difficult. We feel a force pushing us back and we have to lean forward to counteract this force. In a dive the opposite happens. Now we feel a force which pushes us forward and we have to lean backward to counteract this force.

In all three situations the same force was acting, namely, the force of gravity. But by observing exactly the same physical

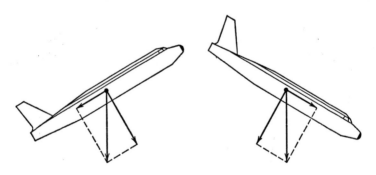

Figure 7

situation from three different frames of reference, we obtain three different descriptions. In the first case the force acts vertically downward, without any horizontal component. In the second and third case we can measure the presence of a horizontal force (horizontal relative to the cabin) in addition to the vertical force.

In psychology we use the word "projection" if one person tries to identify himself with another person (that is, if he tries to put himself in another person's shoes). In physics we use a somewhat different terminology. We say that we "transform" our measurements from one frame of reference to another. To know how this transformation is accomplished is obviously of great importance, and at first sight we may think that it is an easy matter. After all, since we are operating with Cartesian systems of various orientation, it should not be too difficult to obtain the relation between the measurements made in the various systems purely on the basis of the laws of elementary geometry.

In actual fact, the situation in the case of physical (in contrast to purely geometrical) measurements is much more difficult. In physics the element of *change* is added to the space relations of geometry. Our geometrical measurements are constantly changing because of the presence of *time*. We can set up our Cartesian axes in any orientation we like, but now we must take into consideration that these axes will generally be in a state of *motion*. And here something unexpected happens. We might think that, just as in geometry, we should be allowed to operate with arbitrarily oriented Cartesian frames, no matter how this orientation changes in time. But no, this is not so.

Newton's fundamental law of motion is this: "mass times acceleration equals moving force." This "moving force" is not something man-made. It belongs to the physical universe and is thus of absolute significance. Then the "acceleration" should also be of absolute significance, but this is not so. Suppose we measure the acceleration with which a stone falls to the ground. We find that it is 32 feet per second squared, because of the force of gravity with which the earth pulls that stone. But now let us assume that an astronaut, who is in orbit around the earth, makes the same measurement. In his capsule the force of gravity is completely annihilated. Bodies have no weight; a stone released remains suspended in air instead of falling to the ground. In other words, his measurement would not corroborate Newton's law of motion because he measures the acceleration *zero* instead of 32 feet per second squared, in spite of the fact that the force of gravity is still there and that the stone actually does fall toward the earth with the usual acceleration of 32 feet per second squared (slightly less if he is at great heights, due to the diminished pull of the earth). However, since he himself has the same accelerated motion, he has the illusion that the stone remains permanently at rest because, relative to him, it does.

Newton's answer to this difficulty is this: "The fundamental law of motion, mass times acceleration equals moving force, holds only if we are in the right frame of reference. If we move relative to that frame (except if our motion happens to be absolutely uniform, that is, of constant velocity), we destroy the validity of the fundamental dynamical law of physics." Now here is something that is difficult to swallow. What is, after all, a "frame of reference"? Could it be more than a man-made artifice, an auxiliary tool we have manufactured in order to describe the physical universe? Why should we not have the right to relate our measurements to any arbitrary frame of axes we may choose? These axes do not belong to the objective world order. We set up our axes as a kind of scaffold in order to walk on it and be able to reach any part of the building. Yet we must be aware of the fact that this scaffold is not part of the building. It can be put up and pulled down without altering the building in the least. But in Newton's physics the peculiar thing happened that an *absolute frame* was designated (not entirely, since a strictly *uniform motion* relative to it was tolerated) as the only correct frame to which our measurements should be related.

This does not mean that we cannot use other frames of reference as well. For example, it is perfectly legitimate to set up our measuring instruments on our earth which rotates around its axis and does not represent an absolute frame. But the fundamental equation of motion no longer holds and we must take into account the effect on the equation "mass times acceleration equals moving force" of the transformation from the absolute frame to the laboratory frame participating in the earth's rotation. We then obtain a new law of motion which says, "mass times acceleration equals moving force, plus two new forces which are generated by the rotation of our reference system. The one is called 'centrifugal force,' the other 'Coriolis force.'" With this correction we are now safe in making our measurements on the rotating earth, in spite of not being in the right frame of reference. Generally, whenever we are in a wrong frame of reference, we have to add to the moving force some so-called "apparent forces," which are caused solely by the motion of the reference system. For example, in the case of the astronaut in orbit the force of gravity has to be complemented by an apparent force which is accidentally exactly equal to the force of gravity but with the opposite sign, so that the resultant total force becomes zero. This explains why the astronaut becomes weightless in his capsule and why he sees the stone floating freely in air, instead of falling to the ground with an acceleration of 32 feet per second^2.

While it is true that by the addition of apparent forces we overcome the difficulty that the original equation of Newton holds only in an absolute frame, yet we cannot feel satisfied. It is philosophically unsound to designate a certain frame of reference as *the* correct frame. We can hardly accept the notion of an "absolute frame of reference." It looks as if in erecting a building the scaffold became so firmly cemented to the building that it cannot be removed without the entire building collapsing.

✳ Newton's system is based on the assumption of an absolute space and an absolute time. These concepts are logically acceptable. But to assume that in that absolute space there exists a preferential reference system of absolute significance cannot be considered as truly acceptable. How can we imagine that a certain system of coordinates—which is in truth not more than an empty frame, constructed by us solely for the purpose of orientation and identification—should play a vital role in the formulation of the laws of physics? The existence of such a frame was accepted on purely pragmatic grounds, because the consequences of Newton's system seemed to agree with the observed facts. We became reconciled to the idea that the world is simply "made that way" and we could have no quarrel with anything demonstrated by physical experiments. Nevertheless, this was not a very satisfactory answer and a certain feeling of discomfort, keenly felt by Newton himself, could not be shed.

Einstein thought that this fundamental weakness of Newton's system must be corrected. A mere "frame of reference" should not become an integral part of the physical universe; it must remain a mere tool for describing it. Thus he came to the formulation of his celebrated "principle of general relativity," which demanded the following: "It should be possible to formulate the laws of the physical universe in such fashion that they should hold in all possible frames of reference."

This principle of Einstein, which came to fruition in his famous "theory of general relativity," was often misunderstood. Many authors have claimed that this principle is entirely vacuous since an arbitrary equation can be written down in any reference system we want. This claim misses the point, however.

For the proper discussion of our problem a few technical expressions have to be learned. We use the word "invariant" (that which does not change with the frame of reference) when we refer to a certain quantity—such as the mass of a body—which is independent of any particular choice of coordinates. On the other hand, we use the word "covariant" when we refer to a quantity which depends on the coordinates used and changes if we move from one reference system to another. A velocity, for example, is a "covariant" quantity because it has a different value if we measure it in a system which is in relative motion to us. If we say that "our equations remain invariant with respect to arbitrary coordinate transformations," this shall mean that we have equations which hold generally in all systems of coordinates. The principle of general relativity demands that in fact all properly formulated equations of physics should have this property. Otherwise they cannot be considered as a true expression of a law of nature. While we can certainly observe the same physical phenomenon from an infinity of reference systems and thus obtain an infinity of different measurements, it is nevertheless unthinkable that the physical law itself should be influenced by the fact that the observer is in this or that frame of reference.

Let us now examine as an example Newton's fundamental law of mechanics: "mass times acceleration equals moving force." It is certainly true that by the proper mathematical manipulations we can reformulate this equation in an arbitrary frame of reference. But this does not bring the law in harmony with the principle of relativity, because the general formulation of the equation involves quantities which refer to the original reference system from which we started. For example, in writing down Newton's equation for an observer attached to the moving earth, the velocity of the rotation of the earth about its axis enters our equation; however, this velocity can only be measured as *rotation relative to the absolute system*, since a rotation *per se* does not exist. According to the principle of general relativity, a truly acceptable description of a physical law is only attained if we have the right to choose *any* reference system we want, *without* making use of quantities which do not belong to that system. Every reference system must be able to stand on its own feet, without referring to measurements which belong to another system. Only then would we be taking account of the philosophically self-evident fact that a frame of reference is not more than an auxiliary tool of description which cannot be considered as part of the physical law itself.

This does not mean, however, that in a given problem we should not apply a special reference system which is particularly well suited to that problem. The law according to which the planets revolve around the sun becomes infinitely simpler in expression if we choose the sun as the center of our reference system, and not the earth, because the sun has a much larger *mass* than the planets. We have to insist, however, that this practical preference for a particular system should not mean that we are *unable* to formulate the laws of planetary motion in an arbitrary frame. First we must find an equation which describes the planetary motion in "generally covariant form"—the expression "generally covariant" referring to the fact that the equation may be formulated in an arbitrary reference system, without the use of extraneous quantities which do not belong to that reference system. *Then* we can make a wise choice concerning that particular frame of reference in which we are going to solve our problem, in view of the simplicity with which the formal solution will appear in that particular system.

Einstein's program was of tremendous significance and its realization by no means as simple as it might seem today, when we are no longer aware of the great struggle toward clarity which preceded the final result. But the argumentation was so convincing that in a few years time the older Newtonian concepts of an absolute space and absolute time were buried forever and replaced by the new relativistic concepts. This brings to mind a witty aphorism of the philosopher Schopenhauer who once said: "A scientific truth goes through three phases of development. In the first phase it is rejected as absurd. In the second phase it is admitted as a possible hypothesis which has been suggested many times before. In the third phase it is accepted as self-evident." Fifty years ago Einstein's great thought constructions appeared to many people as complete non-sense, as a plain hoax, calculated to impress the physicists with a flood of crazy paradoxes. Twenty years later people said, well, if Einstein wants to write his equations in generally covariant form, why not, he is entitled to do so; mathematics has solved that problem a long time ago, in a chapter of mathematics called "absolute calculus" or "tensor calculus," which deals exactly with the problem of formulating equations in arbitrary coordinate systems. Another twenty years and the idea of general covariance had become so firmly ingrained in the conscience of theoretical physics that if a physicist dares to write down an equation which is not generally covariant, his colleagues will look at him and say: "How can you hope that these equations have any physical significance if they do not satisfy the principle of general relativity?" Indeed, some equations of present-day quantum field physics suffer from the fact that they do not seem to yield to the principle of general covariance, thus causing no end of headaches to the theoreticians.

Finally we discuss a point of particular significance. Newton's concept of an absolute space and an absolute time cannot be brought into harmony with the demand of general covariance. If space and time are independent of each other, the existence of preferential reference systems cannot be avoided. But Einstein's relativity theory of 1905—reformulated in geometrical language by Minkowski in 1908—brought about a radical change. It was perhaps an exceptionally fortunate circumstance that Einstein was primarily a physicist and not a mathematician. Had he perceived the problem in purely mathematical terms, he might have stopped with the theory of 1905 and never advanced to the much more sweeping later theory. The equations of special relativity are such that they can be rewritten in generally covariant form, making use of the formal tools of the mathematical doctrine of absolute calculus. In this case he would have missed the much more grandiose discovery of 1915 which introduced an entirely new type of geometry, called "Riemannian geometry," into the realm of theoretical physics. This discovery came about because the mathematical mechanism was for Einstein of secondary importance. It is certainly true that tensor calculus teaches us how to formulate our equations in such a way that they hold in arbitrary reference systems. But the question of reference systems—important as it was—was not the main concern of Einstein. It was only a departure point which, however, provided him with a very important clue. Einstein noticed that all the apparent forces which come into being whenever we make our measurements in a reference system not in agreement with Newton's absolute system have the peculiar property that they are always strictly proportional to the mass of the moving body. On the other hand, here is that mysterious "gravitational force" of Newton which reveals exactly the same property. Why is it that every mass by its very existence attracts every other mass in strict proportionality to its mass? Why is it that every mass by its very existence has two so utterly different functions: on the one hand it is the seat of inertia, on the other the seat of the force of gravity. The strict proportionality of the attracting force with the mass indicated that there must exist a deep-seated relation between inertia and gravity. Could it be that the "force of gravity" is not a real force at all, but one of the apparent forces which arise if we make our measurements in an accelerated frame of reference? This would immediately explain why the Newtonian force is always proportional to the mass of the moving body.

This mighty idea stirred Einstein's imagination and did not let him rest. He soon saw that the Minkowskian form of geometry—and thus his relativity theory of 1905—could not solve the problem. But if this form of geometry was too restricted, what else could we put in its place?

It was at this juncture that Einstein learned from his friend Grossmann about the great geometrical discoveries of the nineteenth century mathematicians Gauss and Riemann. The geometry conceived by Gauss and fully developed by Riemann came as a godsend to Einstein. Here was a geometry whose concepts were in fullest harmony with that field concept which since the beginning of the last century became more and more dominant in the constructions of theoretical physics, gradually replacing the idea of isolated particles which characterized Newton's physics. The intensive study of this new type of geometry led Einstein to the startling discovery that the simplest geometry which goes beyond Euclid's geometry has all the properties which are demanded by Newton's gravitational theory. He was thus led by logical necessity to his celebrated gravitational equations which gave a full account of all phenomena of gravity on a purely geometrical basis. The single fundamental quantity of Newtonian gravity was replaced by *ten* fundamental quantities, characterized by an infinitely more complex set of equations. But this astonishing theory, arrived at by inspired speculation, now resolved into geometry not only all the physical facts of the 1905 theory, caused by the unification of space and time, but also all the astronomical facts concerning gravitation and the motion of celestial bodies under the action of gravitation. The phenomenon of universal attraction became now an inevitable consequence of that particular form of Riemannian geometry which is realized in the physical universe.

DISCUSSION

QUESTION. If Huygens already understood the relativity of reference systems, why did it take so long after Newton's time to develop the theory of relativity?

ANSWER. There is a great difference between seeing a problem and finding its solution. Newton himself saw clearly that the assumption of an "absolute reference system" cannot be considered as satisfactory from the logical point of view, but his argument was that it can be supported by experimental evidence. The evolution of science is dominated by its inherent laws. Many people before Einstein pondered the problem of reference systems, but the time was not ripe for its solution. In fact, no such solution would have been possible before the unification of space and time which came only under the impact of the puzzle posed by the Michelson-Morley experiment and its successful resolution by Einstein in 1905. Without this step all relativistic speculations would be doomed to failure in advance. The historical evolution was thus logically determined and could not have come sooner.

QUESTION. Is not the appeal to physical intuition, as illustrated by Huygens' approach to the problem of collision, weakened by such work as that done by Yang and Lee who proposed that the laws of nature do distinguish between a system and its mirror image?

ANSWER. The experiments you refer to involve material particles and can hardly be interpreted as a left-right bias existing in empty space. But even if such a bias should exist on a microscopic scale, it is certainly negligible on a macroscopic scale. In the argument of Huygens the balls are replaced by mere points which have no extension. This idealization is certainly much more serious than the assumption of left-right symmetry, even if we imagine that the geometry of nature does not satisfy that principle with absolute accuracy. Every deduction of physics involves some idealization and simplification, compared with the infinite complexity of the actual situation.

QUESTION. It has been suggested that, as the universe ages, the presence of distant matter may weaken the gravitational force at any point. If this view of a time-varying gravitational force is supported by experiments, there would appear to be a contradiction of Einstein's theory of gravitation. Is it possible to reconcile these two points of view? If not, would this not cast doubt upon the advisability of viewing any of Einstein's work as "closing the door" on revisions of either a minor or major nature?

ANSWER. Science knows no dogmatism and under no circumstances can one take the view that Einstein's theory—on authoritarian grounds —might "close the door" on further progress. Anybody has the right to invent whatever theories he likes and claim that they are superior to Einstein's. There are many people who do not care for Einstein and continue to work with purely Newtonian models. As to such delicate effects as the change of the gravitational force at a certain point after billions of years, this may follow from an Einsteinian viewpoint at least as easily as from a Newtonian viewpoint. Einstein himself was not overly interested in such problems, since they involve the question of how matter is distributed in the interstellar spaces and this is something about which we know next to nothing, either theoretically or experimentally.

3

The Unification of Space
and Time by Einstein
and Minkowski

*From this hour on space as such and time as such shall recede
to the shadows and only a kind of union of the two retain significance.*

    H. MINKOWSKI (1908)

TOWARD THE END of the nineteenth century a very peculiar difficulty occupied the greatest minds in the field of theoretical
physics. It was an experimentally and theoretically established
fact that light was a wave phenomenon, in many respects similar
to the acoustical waves observed in air. The speed of propagation was about a million times faster, but nevertheless the wave
nature of light, and also of electricity, could not be doubted.
Since the acoustical waves demand air for their propagation,
another, tremendously light medium, called "ether," was assumed
to be the medium in which the waves of electricity and optics
were propagated.

Let us now assume that an airplane flies in still air. By
watching objects on the surface of the earth, the pilot can easily
determine his velocity relative to the earth. But he can also
measure the same velocity by sending out acoustical signals in

various directions. If he flies with, let us say, one-half sound velocity, the sound waves will propagate relative to him with one-half sound velocity *in* the direction of the flight, and with one and one-half times sound velocity *opposite* to the direction of the flight. If he lets an acoustical signal reflect from a mirror (Figure 8) in the direction of the flight and from another mirror at an equal distance perpendicular to it, then it will take the signal a little longer time to go from O to A and return to O than to go from O to B and return to O. By measuring this little time difference the pilot can determine his velocity relative to the air, even without any ground measurements, although the method requires very accurate instrumentation.

The same reasoning can be applied to optical signals, although the million-times-faster propagation of light makes the experiment much more delicate. But this is no hindrance since the instruments used in spectroscopy have an uncanny accuracy. It was the ingenious American physicist Albert Michelson (there seems to be some black magic in the name Albert) who perfected the accuracy of optical instruments to a fantastic degree (he could measure, for example, the diameters of stars which are hundreds of light years away—a task which is equivalent to measuring 1 inch from a distance of 400 miles). Since we know from astro-

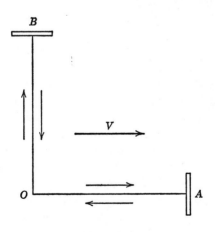

Figure 8

nomical data that the earth revolves around the sun with a speed
of 18 miles per second, it was logical to expect that this speed
would come into evidence if a mirror instrument of the type described above were employed. The famous "Michelson-Morley
experiment" was performed in Cleveland in the year 1887 (it received its name because the chemist Morley participated in the
preparation of the experiment), with an absolutely negative result; no trace of the earth's motion could be detected, although
even one hundredth of the expected result would still have been
measurable. After that many similar optical and electrical experiments were performed with even increased accuracy and none
of them showed even the slightest indication of the expected effect
of the earth's motion. Everything occurred exactly as if the
earth were at rest and the optical and electrical waves were propagated in every direction with the same speed. The expected
addition and subtraction of the earth's velocity to the velocity of
light simply did not take place.

This was a sensational result which put theory in an embar-
rassed position. No flaw in the argumentation could be found
and yet the experimental result contradicted the theoretical prediction in no uncertain terms. Something seemed fundamentally
wrong. Some people thought that perhaps the earth "drags the
ether along" and thus the motion of the earth relative to the ether
could not be detected. But this desperate hypothesis was barred
by other much larger phenomena which could only be explained
on the basis of a "stationary ether," that is, an ether at rest.
The Dutch physicist H. A. Lorentz—and independently the Irish
physicist G. F. Fitzgerald—proposed the explanation that all our
lengths are contracted in the direction of motion, because of the
action of electric forces; this contraction is such that it exactly
nullifies the expected effect. However, while this explanation
would have sufficed as a reason for the negative result of the
Michelson experiment, it still left the door open to other effects
by which the earth's absolute motion could have been detected.
But all other tests were equally negative. It looked as if we
should have to say that nature finds a particular delight in in-
venting the most complicated Rube Goldberg schemes for the sole

purpose of making the motion of the earth through the ether undetectable.

Einstein's paper of 1905 approached the problem from an entirely different point of view. He realized that the decisive question was not whether the ether is at rest or not. Something much more fundamental was at work here. The "ether" as a material medium—which may move or may not move—did not enter his discussion at all. His argument was as follows. What we tried to demonstrate by the Michelson-Morley experiment was the "absolute motion" of the earth. We assumed the existence of an absolute frame of reference, called the "ether," relative to which motion can occur, and this motion should be detectable by properly designed experiments. On the other hand, we know from the principles of mechanics that no absolute motion can ever be detected in the realm of mechanical phenomena. If a train moves on its tracks with perfect smoothness, with uniform velocity, we can never detect its motion if we do not look out of the windows. An acceleration or deceleration is detectable, but a train moving with constant speed cannot give rise to any physically observable phenomenon. Everything happens exactly as if the train were at rest. If we look out of the window, we can discover our motion relative to the earth, but this is not absolute motion because it makes no difference whether we say that the earth is at rest and we move forward, or that we are at rest and the earth moves backward. These two descriptions are absolutely equivalent. In the one case we set up our frame of reference on the earth and see the train moving forward; in the other case we set up our frame of reference on the train and see the earth moving backward. From the standpoint of the physical world one frame of reference is just as acceptable as the other. Absolutely no preference exists. It is true that in Newton's physics we have an absolute frame of reference if it comes to *accelerated* motions, such as the rotation of the earth around its axis. But if we do not leave the realm of motions which occur with constant speed in a constant direction, the principle of relativity is satisfied. And what is that principle? It is that there is no preference among reference systems which move relative to each other with constant velocity. Any one of these reference systems is equally suited for the description of physical phenomena.

If we accept the validity of this principle, then, of course, the negative result of the Michelson experiment is nothing miraculous. It was the purpose of that experiment to measure the velocity of the earth relative to the "ether," which established a preferential reference system. If such a preferential reference system does not exist, there is no absolute motion and it makes no sense to measure the velocity of the earth; in fact, the concept loses all significance.

Now this principle of relativity—that is, the equal admissibility of all reference systems which move with constant velocity relative to each other—was nothing new in physics. It was an important feature of Newtonian mechanics. Einstein merely extended this principle by assuming that it is a *universal* principle of nature, which includes the totality of *all* phenomena, not only the mechanical ones. This in itself was not such a revolutionary innovation. Nevertheless, it demonstrated a remarkably penetrating analysis of the experimental facts. Why should we look for more or less artificial explanations of the negative result of the Michelson-Morley experiment before formulating the true significance of this experiment, which lies in the simple and easily acceptable fact that nature does not admit the existence of an absolute velocity?

The detractors of Einstein pointed out that he did not establish anything new with this hypothesis. The French mathematician Poincaré enunciated the same idea in a lecture given in 1900, and in fact the expression "principle of relativity" first appeared on that occasion. Einstein was not aware of this lecture of Poincaré, but he would have been the last to claim credit for something that somebody else had done before him. The fundamental difference is, however, that Poincaré outlined a program which should be followed, without finding its solution, while Einstein gave the actual solution.

The enunciation of the principle of relativity as a fundamental principle of nature does *not* constitute Einstein's great achievement. His theory rests on two pillars and so far we have mentioned only *one*. The second fundamental demand or "postulate" of Einstein is this: "Light travels in every direction with the same constant velocity, in every legitimate reference system."

Our earth, although in uniform motion (the very slight curvature of the path around the sun is here negligible), represents a legitimate frame of reference, according to the first principle of relativity. If there existed the slightest deviation from a uniform propagation of light in all directions, the Michelson-Morley experiment would have shown it. The second postulate of Einstein is thus nothing but the theoretical formulation of the experimental facts, observed by Michelson and many others, who tried to measure an inhomogeneous propagation of light and found nothing.

It was the juxtaposition and simultaneous application of these two principles which stirred up so much animated controversy and antagonism, and was so often misunderstood. In order to see the true implications of the problem, let us compare light with a fugitive who wants to escape the clutches of the law. A light source emits light (the fugitive) which travels with the speed of 186,000 miles per second. We send a police car after this light signal with orders to catch up with it. This police car is racing ahead with 99 per cent light velocity and its passengers think they are within easy reach of the light signal, which is only 1 per cent of the original velocity ahead of them. And if they speed up their velocity to 99.9 per cent light velocity, they have almost caught up with the fugitive, which now moves ahead with only 0.1 per cent of the original velocity. But no, says Einstein's second postulate. The police car did not accomplish anything at all. If the travelers inside the car measure the velocity of light, they find that light travels relative to them with the full speed of 186,000 miles in every direction, exactly as if they were not moving at all. This is so whether they travel with 50 per cent, or 90 per cent, or 99 per cent, or 99.99 per cent of light velocity. We can never tamper with light velocity. We can move as fast or as slow as we like, the velocity of light is an *absolute constant* of nature which can never be altered.

The first postulate of Einstein claimed that there is no absolute motion and thus the racing police car is just as good a reference system as that in which the light signal was emitted. The second postulate of Einstein demanded that the propagation of light with the full light velocity in every direction hold not only in the system in which the light was emitted but also in the system of the racing car, which is also a legitimate reference system. We could also change the experiment and emit a light signal from the racing car in the direction of the motion (for example, by switching on the headlights). Since the car itself moves with almost light velocity, we would think that relative to us the light velocity has practically doubled. But this is not so. If we measure the velocity of the emitted light, we once more find the old, untampered value of 186,000 miles per second, the simple light velocity, without any modification. It looks almost like the impossible equation

$$1 + 1 = 1$$

It took courage to enunciate two postulates which, taken together, looked on the surface like complete logical non-sense. The addition of velocities goes completely haywire. We add up two light velocities and get only the single light velocity. Common sense tells us that such a thing cannot be done.

Let us assume that we are watching a ship from the shore. The ship moves at a speed of 10 miles per hour. Somebody walks on the deck at a rate of 2 miles per hour, in the direction of the ship's motion. What will be his velocity relative to us? Common sense tells us that it will be 12 miles per hour. If he walks backward, his velocity relative to us will be 8 miles per hour. Is there anything simpler than that? Can anybody find a flaw in this argument?

Common sense is not always a good guide, however, in scientific matters. Over and over in the history of science we have seen how deceptive "common sense" can be. Aristotle accepted the product of mass times velocity as the measure of force. Velocity is something very plausible and common sense. It took almost 2000 years before the much more remote and less palpable *acceleration* was dug out as the true measure of force. When Copernicus taught the rotation of the earth around its axis and the revolution of the planets around the sun, people thought on the ground of common sense that he had lost his mind. If the earth were really moving—common sense tells us—this motion would create such a wind that it would blow away the roofs of our houses. A stone thrown vertically upward would land way behind, etc. Little children in school have the hardest time trying to understand how unity, which is obviously indivisible, can be divided by 2 or 3 or 4, in order to obtain ½, ⅓, ¼. Later they learn to subtract 5 from 3, when common sense tells us that such a thing is obviously impossible. The shock is hardly over when they have to take the square root of minus 1. In all these cases something has to be accepted which is against all the rules of common sense. As late as 1637 Descartes in his famous *Géometrie* draws an ellipse as shown in Figure 9 because he was afraid of using negative coordinates.

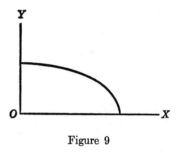

Figure 9

The fact is that common sense is far from being a satisfactory basis of scientific thinking. The mathematical and physical sciences demand the most uncommon kind of thinking imaginable. No scientific discovery was ever made by the application of common sense.

It took the great boldness of Einstein's scientific imagination to perceive that the two postulates on which the special theory of relativity is based are logically contradictory only if we accept Newton's axioms of an absolute space and an absolute time. The two postulates that he enunciated were not made up in order to impress his colleagues with some startling paradoxes. They were distilled by a careful analysis from a large number of well-established physical measurements. But if we accept these two postulates, we see at once that Newton's absolute space and absolute time have to be abandoned. In our previous example of the moving ship and the walking man the addition of the two velocities would indeed be inevitable if we accept as an inevitable fact that the time measurements on the shore and on the moving ship must necessarily be the same. Yet this need not be so. Is it not possible that one reference system moving relative to another has its own space and time measurements which need not coincide with the others? If we take it as an unalterable fact that the only possible relation between the time t measured in the one system and the time t' measured in the other system can be

$$t = t',$$

then the two postulates of relativity are indeed self-contradictory. But if we drop this assumption and take the unprejudiced viewpoint that the one observer has his *four* coordinates

$$x, \ y, \ z, \ t,$$

and the other observer his four coordinates

$$x', \ y', \ z', \ t',$$

then we can find out what kind of relations must exist between these quantities in order to satisfy the two fundamental postulates. Einstein showed that the two pillars of relativity are in fact sufficient to obtain a very definite relation between the two sets of quantities. The resulting equations do not coincide with the customary equations which were in use for hundreds of years. However, if the velocities involved are small compared with light velocity, the correction to the usual formulae becomes exceedingly small and we do not come in contradiction with the fact that physics could go along very well for a long time on the basis of Newton's absolute time, without relativity. If, for example, we calculate on the basis of the celebrated "Einstein's addition law of velocities," what happens in the previously given example to the two numbers 12 and 8, we find that the figure 8 becomes slightly larger, the figure 12 slightly smaller. However, the correction is incomprehensibly small because we have to change 8 to a number in which we have to write after the 8 twenty-five zeros and then a 7, while instead of 12 we have to write 11, followed by twenty-five nines and then a 3. These are immeasurably small differences. But this is no longer the case if we observe very light particles which move very fast, with velocities approaching that of light. In that case the corrections demanded by the theory of relativity become very noticeable and the Newtonian laws of motion go completely out of order.

Einstein drew all the physical consequences of his theory and showed that they are in complete harmony with the observed physical facts and measurements. Certain additional predictions concerning the motion of very fast particles could not be tested at that time but later became of greatest importance when the construction of the cyclotron and other devices for the production of particles of very high speed made it imperative to calculate the paths of particles at speeds approaching light velocity. The formulae of relativity were fully corroborated under the most exacting conditions by the fact that the instruments built on the basis of the relativistic formulae performed exactly as predicted.

Yet the most spectacular and in its consequences most tragic conclusion of relativistic speculations was Einstein's celebrated equation $E = mc^2$. It was known since the time of Newton and Leibniz that a given mass m, if in motion, represents a definite amount of energy, namely $\frac{1}{2} mv^2$, if v is the velocity of the mass. This form of energy was called "kinetic energy," that is, the energy due to motion. But this energy disappeared if the mass came to rest. Now the theory of relativity demanded—as Einstein demonstrated as early as 1905 in incomplete form, and in 1907 in its final form—that the mass m by its very existence is the source of a tremendous amount of energy, compared with which the kinetic energy was not more than a small correction. This vast store of energy does not come into play under ordinary circumstances because of the great stability of the mass m. What we measure experimentally are always energy *differences,* and thus an added constant in the expression of the energy must remain undetected. But this unification of two previously separate entities, mass and energy, had far-reaching consequences. If mass is not more than a form of energy, our assumption of the indestructible nature of mass needs revision. The sum of the energies is conserved but there are many forms in which energy may manifest itself. Hence the possibility could be envisaged that a given mass as mass may be destroyed and converted into another form of energy.

This possibility opened up a new perspective for the solution of one of the most vexing problems of physics, the one dealing with the origin of solar energy. What is the source of the incredibly vast energy constantly emitted by the sun and the stars in the form of radiation? With the possibility of converting mass into radiation—one form of energy into another—a new source of energy came into sight. Perhaps the sun (and also the stars) gradually decrease in mass because it is their mass which is converted into radiation? The latent energy value of a mass is certainly an immense quantity, because of the multiplication by the huge factor c^2. One gram of matter represents an energy of 25 million kilowatt hours, that is, the energy used by a 3 kilowatt electric heater which burns day and night continuously for 2000 years. Here then is an energy source which is almost inexhaustible, sufficient to provide the sun's radiation energy for billions of years to come, without reducing its mass by more than a tiny fraction of its present value.

Later research revealed that it is more specifically the nuclear change of hydrogen into helium that releases the sun's energy. The atomic mass of helium, compared with hydrogen, is 3.971 and and thus, if four hydrogen nuclei come together and unite into a helium nucleus, the new mass is not 4 but only 3.97, leaving a "mass defect" of about 1 per cent of the original mass, which is converted into radiation. This reaction takes place at a tremendous temperature of at least 20 million degrees centigrade in the core of the sun.

Nobody could have foreseen around 1905 that this fundamental conclusion of relativity would some day become the gravest danger to the survival of the human race. But the successful production of the "atom bomb"—based on the breaking up of the uranium-235 nucleus into two smaller fragments with a mass defect of about 0.1 per cent of the original mass—made it possible to create a temperature of 50 million degrees centigrade, and the change of hydrogen into helium became a reality under terrestrial conditions. The H-bomb thus constructed has an explosive power which surpassed that of the uranium bomb by a factor of 1000 and more, and we are still far from the end of the road.

All these terrifying demonstrations of Einstein's mass-energy equivalence corroborated the awe-inspiring consistency which manifests itself in the mathematical structure of the universe, together with the mortal dangers which accrue if the results of inspired cosmic meditations are converted into purely pragmatic aims.

A few years later (1908–09) Hermann Minkowski discovered the deeper significance of the relativistic postulates. He did not change any of the substance of Einstein's work, but translated Einstein's ideas from the world of physics into the world of geometry. The idea of representing time in a geometrical manner is not so new. We are all familiar with those instruments which record the daily temperature from hour to hour in the form of a "graph." Here we read off the time on the abscissa and the corresponding temperature on the ordinate. Time is plotted in this graph (Figure 10) as a *length*. We are also familiar with the well-known sales curves which show how a certain brand of automobile, for example, has sold through the years. On the abscissa we see the years marked, on the ordinate the number of cars sold. Once more time has been plotted as length.

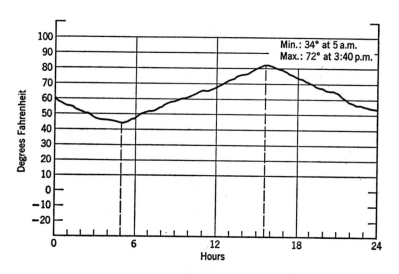

Figure 10

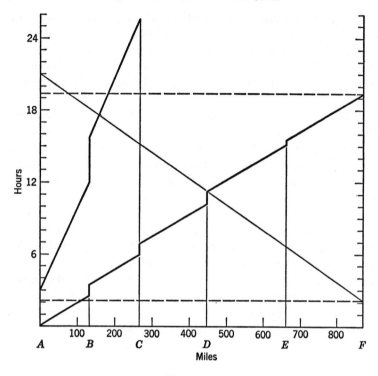

Figure 11

Still another example is provided by the so-called "graphic time tables." On the horizontal we plot the miles between two stations, such as New York and Chicago, for example, and on the vertical we plot the time (Figure 11). A train leaving New York at midnight and arriving in Chicago at 19:30 hours is represented by a straight line if the train moves constantly with the same speed. If the train stops at certain stations, we get broken lines because the time passes on without any motion, that is, without changing the position of the train on the abscissa. Of course, the train could not stop suddenly from full speed, nor could it attain full speed after starting from zero velocity. This means that instead of getting sharp corners as indicated on the idealized

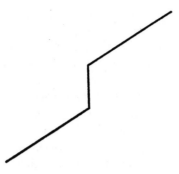

Figure 12

graph (Figure 12), the gradual acceleration and deceleration rounds off these corners and in a realistic representation we would get a picture like that in Figure 13. The important thing is that there is no physical detail of the actual motion which would not be represented by some geometrical detail of the graph. The slower the train, the steeper its graph becomes, the angle reaching 90 degrees if the train stands still and nearly 0 degrees if the train moves very fast, because in the first case time passes without any change in distance, while in the second case even in a short time the change in distance is very great.

Now Minkowski's idea was that this plotting of the time as an added length is not merely a convenient way of representing for

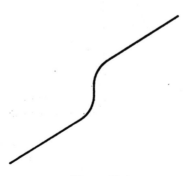

Figure 13

ourselves a train's motion but is something that actually happens in nature. He thus called the graph of the moving train its "world line." We have to imagine that these "world lines" are not merely our method of representing motion in the form of a simple figure but are *actually* realized in the physical world, because in nature the thing that we conceive as "time" is in fact an added geometrical dimension.

Now if we introduce this idea in Newton's physics, we see at once that we obtain a picture reminiscent of the days when the earth was conceived as flat and not as a globe. In that world up and down had an absolute significance, whereas we know that up and down on the earth are of purely local significance because the up and down of a person who lives a thousand miles away appears to us as a slanted line. In Newton's physics time was an absolute quantity and thus, if we represented time along the vertical, the up and down had an absolute and universal significance. We know, however, that it is purely accidental that we draw our abscissa horizontally, our ordinate vertically. We do that purely for aesthetic reasons and not out of an inherent necessity. We could equally well use a pair of axes in a slanted position (Figure 14).

What is the significance of these slanted lines from the physical

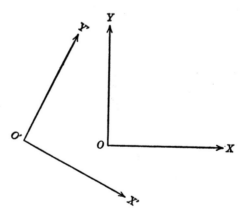

Figure 14

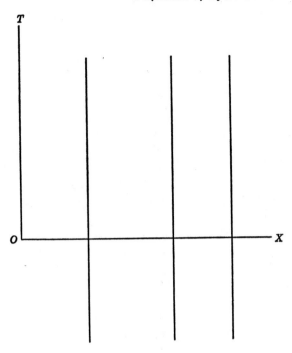

Figure 15

standpoint? Let us go back to our train and see what happens. We imagine that between New York and Chicago there are people standing on the embankment to watch the trains passing by. Now these people do not move and thus their world lines are simply parallel vertical lines (Figure 15). On the other hand, we consider people who travel with this very long train. Since these people all move with the train, with a common speed, their world lines are parallel slanted lines (Figure 16).

Let us now put these two groups of people together. The people of the embankment watch the people of the moving train, and vice versa. We see at once that these two groups of people live in two different worlds as far as space and time is concerned. Let us call the people along the embankment the "*A* people," the people who travel with the train the "*B* people." The *A*

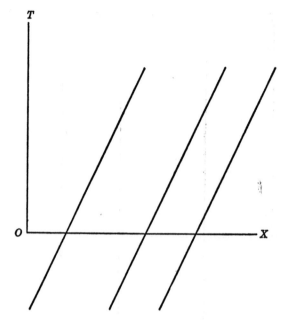

Figure 16

people say: "X is my space axis, T my time axis." The B people say: "X' is my space axis, T' my time axis."

In view of this change of reference systems peculiar things happen. For example, what does it mean if the A people say: "At a certain time moment"? It means a line such as PQ (Figure 17). But what does it mean if the B people say: "At a certain time moment"? It means a line such as $P'Q'$. *What is simultaneous for the people on the embankment is not simultaneous for those on the train, and vice versa.* Let us assume, for example, that the people of the embankment decide to honor the people on the train by exploding a set of flashbulbs along the embankment at exactly the same time moment. Then the people on the train will find that these flashbulbs did *not* go off at the same time moment, but one after the other. The same would happen if the train people conspire to make a display for the

benefit of the embankment people by exploding flashbulbs inside
the train at a certain time moment. The people of the embankment would observe these explosions *in succession,* not simul-
taneously.

Even stranger things happen if the *A* people and the *B* people
compare their clocks. Let us assume that the embankment
people put up a series of clocks along the embankment for the
benefit of the train people. A person traveling on the train takes
out his watch and compares it with the readings of the clocks
outside, as they fly by. He finds to his amazement that those
clocks run much faster than his watch. When his watch has advanced by 10 minutes, the readings on the outside clocks show
an advance of, let us say, 80 minutes (the magnitude of the effect
depends on the speed of the train relative to the embankment).

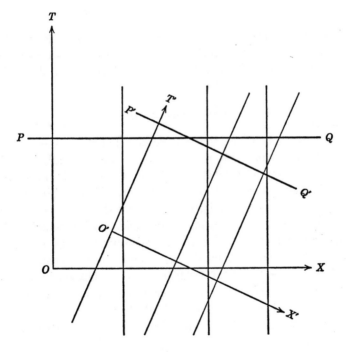

Figure 17

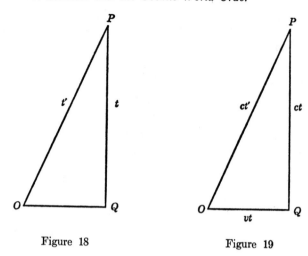

Figure 18   Figure 19

Indeed, while for him the time $t' = \overline{OP}$ has passed (Figure 18), the time shown by the clock at the point Q of the embankment is $t = \overline{QP}$. Now according to our figure, t' is greater than t because by the law of Pythagoras we have

$$\overline{OP^2} = \overline{OQ^2} + \overline{QP^2}$$

It so happens, however, that nature does not do us the favor of making our geometrical model perfect. First of all, in order to consider time as a length, we have to convert it into length by multiplying it by a definite scale factor, which is light velocity (186,000 miles per second), usually denoted by c. This means that we have to take care of the tremendous discrepancy which exists between our usual units for measuring length and time, namely, centimeter (or inch) and second, since 1 second has to be plotted as a length of 186,000 miles, or 300,000 kilometers. Hence first of all we have to change t to ct in our triangle (Figure 19). Furthermore, in nature's Pythagorean law a peculiar *change of sign* takes place. The correct law is not our customary Pythagorean law $\overline{OP^2} = \overline{QP^2} + \overline{OQ^2}$, but

$$\overline{OP^2} = \overline{QP^2} - \overline{OQ^2}$$

Hence, in fact, t' is not *larger* but *smaller* than t, which means that the clock of the train advanced by *less* than the time shown on the clock of the embankment. Here again the difference is immeasurably small for small velocities and a real check can be obtained only with velocities which approach light velocity. The nearer the train approaches light velocity, the smaller t' becomes and if we imagine that the travelers could actually reach light velocity, time for them would stand still. Let us imagine that a traveler is shot out of a cannon with light velocity and proceeds toward the star Sirius which is 8 light years away. When he arrives on Sirius, he is shot back to earth and once more he travels with light velocity. When he arrives back on earth, we on earth have aged 16 years, while he is just as young as when he started. If somebody could circumnavigate the entire universe "on the wings of light," this would take, according to our clocks, billions of years, while he would in fact return to us just as young as when he started.

This so-called "clock paradox" has caused more controversy in the literature than any other scientific controversy. It caught the fancy of the masses, and people of all walks of life, from the humble pariahs of India to the loftiest philosophers of all countries, talked about the "clock paradox." Although the problem first came into prominence around 1920 and Einstein gave a full resolution of it, even today it happens that half-learned journals publish long articles (from the pens of less than half-learned people) which purport to show that Einstein was really a fool. Considering the fact that the conclusions are very much against our ordinary "common sense" thinking and do not harmonize in the least with our usual reasoning habits, many people dismissed the whole problem as a fancy dream which has no relation to the world of facts. Well, they said, if Mr. Einstein wants to cook up some ingenious paradoxes, why not, let him do so, but we do not have to believe him.

Amazingly enough, just a few years ago a perfect confirmation of this consequence of relativity was obtained. True enough, space travel at the moment is still very far from light velocity, and it is improbable that human beings will ever be able to travel with speeds comparable to light velocity. But there are other kinds of space travelers whose testimony is just as reliable as that of human beings. In the atom-smashing experiments of recent years some very light particles, called "mu-mesons," were generated. These mu-mesons have a very short lifetime because they disintegrate very rapidly into some other forms of matter. Their average lifetime—measurable in the laboratory—is in fact not more than 2 millionths of a second. Now these mu-mesons are also generated in exceedingly great heights of the atmosphere, because of bombardments by cosmic rays which come from outer space. It so happens that under the heavy impact of cosmic rays these little particles are tremendously accelerated and reach velocities which are nearly light velocity. They travel toward the earth with a velocity which is 99.5 per cent light velocity. At such immense velocities the relativistic time magnification factor becomes very noticeable. The time measured by the people on the moving train is then only one-tenth of the time measured by the people of the embankment. The "moving train" is now represented by the fast-moving mu-meson, while the "people of the embankment" are we ourselves who make our physical measurements on the earth. Now during the very short lifetime of the mu-meson the distance it can traverse in the atmosphere is not more than 600 meters. Since these cosmic-ray showers occur in very high altitudes, there should be no chance that these mu-mesons will come down to the surface of the earth; they should have disintegrated long before. But now comes the relativistic time factor. The 2 millionths of a second lifetme of the mu-meson becomes enlarged, if measured with our clocks, by the factor 10 and thus becomes 20 millionths of a second. During that time the meson traverses not 600 meters but 6000 meters, that is, 6 kilometers. This distance is sufficient to bring it down to earth and so it becomes explainable that we do find these mu-mesons in cosmic ray shower fragments on the earth, which would be quite impossible without the relativistic time correction.

Actually, the term "clock paradox" usually refers to a very specific situation which looks as if a logical contradiction could be constructed against the consequences of relativity. We imagine two identical twins who perform the following experiment. The one twin remains permanently at rest. The other is shot out of a cannon and travels with almost light velocity to Sirius, there he stops and is shot back to earth (once more with almost light velocity). The one twin who did not leave the earth has aged 16 years, while the space-traveling twin has aged practically not at all. Now how would these two twins describe the experiment? The twin at rest would say: "I see my twin brother moving to the left with light velocity, then he stops and returns to me again with light velocity."

The space-traveling twin says: "I see my twin brother moving to the right with light velocity, then he stops and returns to me again with light velocity." Except for the exchange of the two words "left" and "right," the two descriptions are exactly the same. How then could the consequences be so completely different in the two cases?

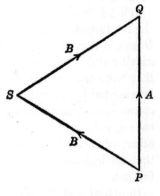

Figure 20

The contradiction comes from the fact that a mere description of an observation need not necessarily be a true assessment of a given physical situation. If an astronaut in orbit revolves once around the earth in 2 hours, he will observe from his capsule that the earth turned around its axis in 2 hours. But the earth turns around its axis in 24 hours and not in 2 hours. In the case of the twins the geometrical picture shows at once that the two brothers are by no means in a symmetrical situation. The world lines of the twins are shown in Figure 20. The world line of *A* (who stayed at rest) is a straight line, the world line of the twin brother *B* (who traveled) is the broken line *PSQ*. The fact that *B* received a tremendous kickback at the point *S* puts him in a completely different situation from *A*. Since the age of the brothers is determined by the lengths of their world lines, we see at once that *A* aged less according to the figure than *B*, the straight line *PQ* being shorter than the broken line *PSQ*. Since, however, we have to exchange "smaller" and "larger" in view of nature's modified Pythagorean law, the final result is that *A* aged more than *B*.

If the two twins actually preserve their physical symmetry by doing the same thing in opposite directions, the nonsymmetry of the result immediately disappears. If *B* travels to the left, *A* to the right, and both of them receive the same kickback at the same time moment, the complete symmetry of the figure demonstrates that both brothers aged by exactly the same amount (Figure 21).

What is so misleading in the analysis of these relations is that the impression is created that the clocks of the *A* people and the *B* people run at different rates. It seems that the clocks on the moving train run *slower* than the clocks of the embankment. If that were true, it is clear that the principle of relativity would be violated because then we could say that the clocks of the reference system *B* run at a slower rate than the clocks of the reference system *A*, thereby distinguishing the one system from the other, whereas we know that the principle of relativity demands that all legitimate reference systems must remain on the same footing.

In actual fact the discrepancy of the time measurements does not originate in the speeds of the clocks—which in fact run in every reference system at the same rate. The discrepancy comes from the fact that these measurements involve completely dif-

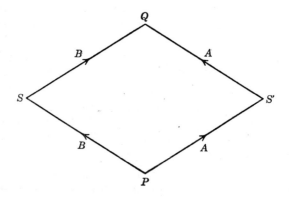

Figure 21

ferent world lines which cannot be "put together" and thus do not allow a direct comparison. Strange as the usual formulation of the clock paradox appears, the following formulation is even more striking. An observer on the fast-moving train looks out of the window and observes the people of the embankment. He is surprised to find how quickly they seem to age. Checking with his watch he says: "Is it not amazing? These people grow a beard in 10 minutes." But let us now reverse the experiment. An observer on the embankment takes out his watch and observes the people on the moving train. Will he say "How *young* these people stay. They do not grow a beard for a very long time"? No. He says: "Amazing, how quickly these people age; they grow a beard in 10 minutes." Indeed, he is in exactly the same situation relative to the people on the moving train as the observer on the moving train is relative to the people on the embankment. It is the *complete reciprocity* of reference systems, their complete "equality before the law," which is the most striking and at the same time most satisfactory feature of the principle of relativity.

In view of the unusually fierce opposition which met Einstein's ideas at the time they first became widely known, and the constant efforts to find flaws in them, we may ask whether it is at all possible that some day an actual contradiction may come into evidence. Since Minkowski's formulation of the theory of relativity has shown that this theory is completely equivalent to an extension of our ordinary geometry from three to four dimensions, we can predict with full confidence that an *inner* contradiction within the theory itself is unthinkable. Such a contradiction would amount to a contradiction within Euclidean geometry itself and the possibility of that we are not prepared to believe (although curiously enough a rigorous proof of the inner consistency of the Euclidean postulates has never been found). What remains then is the possibility that certain consequences of the theory would not check with the physical facts. This, however, would not invalidate the theory because Einstein's general relativity has shown that the original theory of 1905 is only an approximation which in fact can never hold with perfect accuracy, in view of the fact that the geometry of the world is not flat, as Minkowski's geometry would indicate, but curved, due to the presence of matter. Any discrepancy with the world of facts would thus indicate that we have to enlarge our theory toward a still more comprehensive geometry which, however, would once more include space and time.

Under no circumstances would we ever return to Newton's absolute space and absolute time, no matter how much our common sense may sympathize with these concepts. Originally, when Einstein first tackled the problem of reference systems, his ideas seemed in such contradiction to our traditional way of thinking that his conclusions were only accepted under protest, in view of their eminent pragmatic value, but not because we liked them. Yes, we said, the physical facts seem to demonstrate that Einstein is right, but we wish he were wrong. Later, as we gradually saw the light and realized the inherent greatness of the new outlook, the tremendous simplification and unification which came into our picture of the physical world in consequence of Einstein's theories, we accepted his ideas with enthusiasm and would not want to depart from his way of thinking under any circumstances, just as we would never again give up fractions, negative numbers, irrational numbers, complex numbers, or limit processes in the world of mathematics, even if these concepts had not shown their pragmatic value by being so eminently useful in our human endeavors. The fundamental concepts of science develop originally out of a pragmatic necessity. We want to describe the world of reality and for that purpose we need certain strange concepts, such as negative and complex numbers, infinite expansions, and many other tools of mathematical manipulations which at first sight run counter to our common sense notions. But later, as our abstract world of ideas develops, we see the inner necessity of these ideas and the great aesthetic satisfaction we derive from them.

When relativity first appeared on the platform, we were impressed by the fact that it worked, and we were willing to accept it as a kind of necessary evil. Later, with the gradual evolution of a still more comprehensive scheme, the theory of general relativity, we learned to look at Einstein's achievements with a new eye. The fact that it fits the world of facts so admirably is no longer the decisive point. Decisive is the immense philosophical satisfaction that we gain from his ideas. The possibility of understanding the universe from a unified viewpoint becomes by far more important than the mere technical description of observed facts. Behind the accidental facts we recognize the tremendous unity of nature, the existence of a master plan, from which everything follows with inexorable mathematical necessity.

There is a beautiful story told of Benjamin Disraeli, the famous English prime minister of Victorian times, which has a certain bearing on our subject. Disraeli came from a very poor family and thus saw little chance to succeed in life. Since he was a very ambitious young man, bent on making a career, he married a girl who was far from good looking but had plenty of money. The marriage became a great success. Thirty years later, when he was world famous and the first man of the British Empire, somebody asked him how he would have acted now, surrounded by all the money and fame he wanted. His answer was: "At that time I married her for money; today I would marry her for love."

DISCUSSION

QUESTION. What happens to the Lorentz contraction in Einstein's theory?

ANSWER. The Lorentz contraction is no longer a more or less arbitrary assumption but a necessary consequence of the relations which exist between the coordinates of the two reference systems which are in relative motion to each other. A sphere moving with great speed appears as a flattened ellipsoid which collapses into a disk if light velocity is reached. The difference is that in the theory of Lorentz the sphere is *really* contracted to an ellipsoid, because of the motion relative to the ether, while in relativity motion as such does not exist. An observer attached to the sphere perceives the sphere as a sphere, while an observer relative to whom the sphere is in motion perceives the same sphere as an ellipsoid because his space and time measurements differ from those of the other observer who is attached to the sphere.

QUESTION. What is the significance of the constancy of light velocity in Minkowski's geometrical interpretation of Einstein's theory?

ANSWER. The change of sign from plus to minus in nature's Pythagorean law has far-reaching consequences. In a strictly Euclidean world two points can have the distance zero from each other only if the two points collapse into one. In the geometry of Minkowski this is quite different; "zero distance" means in physical terms that a sphere expands (or contracts) with light velocity. Hence light propagation (with the same velocity in every direction) means geometrically the locus of all the points which have the distance zero from the origin. Since "distance" is an absolute quantity which has the same value in all legitimate reference systems, zero distance remains zero distance for all reference systems; this means that the propagation of light with the constant velocity c in every direction remains the same phenomenon for all observers.

QUESTION. What volumetric size $\Delta x \, \Delta y \, \Delta z \, \Delta ct$ is occupied by the observer to which the Einstein-Minkowski four-dimensional geometry applies?

ANSWER. A particle conceived as a point has a definite "world line." In the case of an extended particle each point of the particle has a world line and the entire particle is now represented by a bundle of world lines, or a "world tube." It is this whole tube which has significance for nature. We can cut this tube with planes, determine various cross sections or volumes between cross sections, but all this occurs in view of certain special experiments we perform with the particle. We have to be aware, however, that for nature only the tube as a whole has existence; the special portions to which we pay attention come into play solely because of the experiments we perform. The calculations we make will depend on the reference system we are in and the specific nature of the experiment we perform. The same can be said of the world tube which represents the observer.

QUESTION. I have only heard the twin brother problem discussed in the context of special relativity. But what happens to the space traveler during the period of acceleration? What does general relativity predict for the space traveler?

ANSWER. General relativity did not alter any of the essential features of the analysis of the clock paradox because even in general relativity a clock carried by an observer measures the length of the world line of the observer and the lengths of two lines drawn between the fixed points P and Q can again be different. There is, however, the further interesting possibility that from the standpoint of general relativity the "kickback" at the point S could be provided by the gravitational field of a very heavy star. In that case the twin brothers are in a still more congruent situation inasmuch as now both of them would proceed in a straight line and the break at the point S is no longer needed. But here again the principle of symmetry is not violated because now the star near the point S by its gravitational field creates an asymmetry in the geometry of the universe and the two twin brothers are distinguished by the fact that the one stayed away from the heavy star near S while the other came near to it.

QUESTION. After the layman in physics accepts that the speed of light in a vacuum is an absolute upper bound for all speeds in the universe, he may then be startled to read that in some other media—for instance, some fluids—the speed of light through that medium may be exceeded. In fact there is an effect (called the Cerenkov effect) similar to a shock wave when the speed of light through a medium is exceeded. What, if anything, does this strange phenomenon mean in connection with relativity? It seems hard to understand why in space the speed of light is an absolute bound but in other media not.

ANSWER. The upper limit of all material velocities is c, which is purely a geometrical consequence of the structure of the space-time world. It is, however, also the velocity with which light propagates in a vacuum. In a fluid, light propagates at a lower speed on account of the secondary waves generated by the incoming light wave which excites the electrons of the substance to forced vibrations. Although the propagation velocity of all the elementary waves is still c, the interaction of the primary and secondary waves generates a phase velocity c' which is less than c. The Cerenkov radiation comes about by fast-moving electrons which move faster than c' but not as fast as c. There is no difficulty from the standpoint of relativity since there is no reason why the speed of these electrons should be limited by the velocity c' which characterizes the phase propagation inside the fluid.

4

The Geometrical Discoveries of Gauss

> *Perhaps in another world we may gain other insights into the nature of space which at present are unattainable to us. Until then we must consider geometry as of equal rank not with arithmetic, which is purely logical, but with mechanics, which is empirical.*
>
> C. F. GAUSS (1817)

CARL FRIEDRICH GAUSS (1777–1855) was one of the most prodigious mathematical geniuses of all ages. His unusual mathematical faculties came into evidence from his earliest youth and remained unabated up to his death. Whenever the three greatest mathematicians of all times are enumerated, Gauss is inevitably one of them. His great love was number theory. He used to say: "Mathematics is the queen of the sciences, but number theory is the queen of mathematics." If he could have followed his heart's desire, he would probably have spent all his life in number theoretical speculations. Fortunately for the development of the exact sciences, his official duties brought him in touch with many fields of applied science, in which his uncanny mathematical abilities opened new avenues of research.

His official position was that of an astronomer at the Observatory of Goettingen and the many evenings he spent in painstaking astronomical observations could probably have been spent more profitably in more speculative endeavors. But it was in connection with these observations that he discovered the "method of least squares," which became one of the most fundamental cornerstones of statistical methods. His lecturing at the university was also a burden to him, but these activities brought him in touch with the physicist W. E. Weber (1804–91), an event which had many fortunate consequences for the development of the science of electricity and magnetism. The first electromagnetic telegraph communication in the world was established between the houses of Gauss and Weber, who frequently exchanged friendly morning greetings in coded language. One is somewhat reminded of the legendary King Midas of Greek mythology—whatever he touched turned to gold. Many of the discoveries of Gauss took their origin from some accidental task that was requested of him; perhaps it was a burdensome task but, applying himself to it with his usual thoroughness and exactitude, he brought forth something exceptionally important.

One day he was approached by the Minister of Public Affairs of the little Duchy of Hanover—in whose service he stood—with a request that he supervise a new project. The project was an exact and detailed surveying of the entire Hanoverian district. This became necessary because the many small farmsteads had frequent border litigations and the construction of an accurate land-registry had become of urgent importance.

One would hardly assume that this surveying activity would necessitate the services of a first-class mathematical brain. Gauss was not very happy with this new duty which would burden him with added responsibilities, diverting his energies from other more important problems. Today we feel eminently grateful to the State Administration of Hanover for their decision to ask the participation of Gauss in their geodetic surveying problem. It was in the course of this activity that Gauss made an outstanding geometrical discovery which became of crucial importance for the later development of science. When Einstein started to ponder the problem of general reference systems, he came in touch with the geometrical methods of Gauss. In fact, it was Gauss who forged the tools without which general relativity could not have been developed. How astonishing to think that one of the greatest advances of the human mind became possible because the government of Hanover asked the great mathematician Gauss to help them in their surveying work.

Gauss was, in fact, from his earliest youth interested in the problem of geometry. But why should geometry be a problem at all? Had not the Greeks already solved the problem of geometry by developing that wonderful edifice of exact geometrical thinking called "Euclidean geometry"?

Indeed, for hundreds of years it seemed that nothing essential could be added to the structure of geometry developed by the Greeks. Greek geometry became the pattern of an exact science. Starting from certain basic axioms and postulates, everything could be deduced by purely logical arguments. Hence the entire edifice stands and falls with the axioms and postulates. The Greeks, with their sharp mental faculties and sceptical scientific spirit, paid much attention to the matter of the basic assumptions on which the entire edifice of a certain branch of science rests. They distinguished carefully between "axioms" and "postulates," although many of our dictionaries today give practically identical definitions for both concepts. In the Greek terminology an "axiom" is a statement which cannot be denied without frustrating all possibilities of logical reasoning. Such an axiom is, for example, that equal operations performed on equal quantities give equal results. It is simply logically unimaginable that starting with the same quantities and doing the same operations with them we should arrive at different results. The "axioms" are thus demanded by the nature of our thinking and cannot be the subject of argument. The expression "self-evident truth" was not used by the cautious Greek philosophers who well realized that "self-evident" is not a word which should enter a scientific argument. A better definition of an axiom is: "A statement demanded by the nature of our thinking."

The so-called "postulates" are of an altogether different caliber. They do not refer to the nature of our thinking but express some specific statements which are characteristic for this or that science. Aristotle says that the student accepts the postulates on the authority of the teacher. Although the postulates seem eminently *plausible*, they do not express a logical *necessity*. Euclid does not introduce his postulates by saying: "It is self-evident that," but by saying: "Let it be taken for granted that."

The distinction is of greatest importance, although the postulates of Euclid are so deceptively persuasive that we would be willing to accept them as self-evident. For example, the statement "Between two points only one straight line can be drawn" appears entirely self-evident. We could not imagine that between A and B (Figure 22) a second line could be drawn which is straight. This second line would inevitably have a curvature. Similarly, we would not imagine that a straight line could ever come to an end. Starting from a certain point and always walking in the same direction we could forever continue our walk, never coming to an end. And thus the statement "A straight line is infinite in extension" appears also as self-evident. To the Greeks, however, it was quite clear that the fact that our space perception cannot imagine something does not mean that it is *logically* impossible. The statement that our visual faculties do not permit the existence of a second straight line between A and B does not mean that we could not perceive *logically* the existence of a second straight line.

In the later evolution of history this fine distinction between axioms and postulates became blurred, with disastrous consequences. Even such a keen and deep thinker as Kant fell in

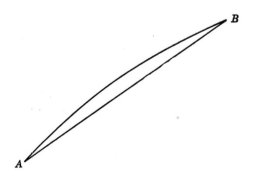

Figure 22

the trap by believing that the postulates of Euclid are of an absolute and incontestable character. The entire Kantian philosophy breaks down because of this single but fundamental mistake.

While nobody could seriously doubt that Euclid is right in assuming the uniqueness and infinity of a straight line, and also in his assumption that space has everywhere the same properties —which makes it possible that figures can be freely moved around without breaking their inner relations—yet there was one additional postulate which caused considerable uneasiness from the beginning. This famous "fifth postulate"—usually referred to as the "parallel postulate"—did not have the simplicity and immediacy of the other postulates and seemed to play the role of an outsider. In a formulation slightly different from that given by Euclid but in essence equivalent to it this postulate asserted that from a point *P* outside of a straight line every line going through *P* will intersect the given straight line, except *one* limiting line which will not intersect the line, neither on the left nor on the right side, and which is thus *parallel* to the given straight line (Figure 23).

Numerous attempts have been made to prove this postulate of Euclid on the basis of the other postulates, but all the alleged "proofs" were based on self-deception. Gauss himself tried in his youth to prove this postulate but soon came to the conclusion that no such proof is in fact possible because, assuming the falsity of this postulate, we would not come into any logical contradic-

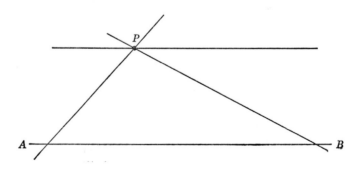

Figure 23

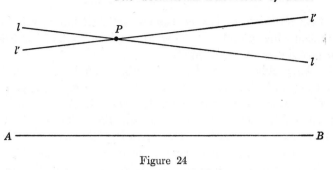

Figure 24

tion with the other postulates. We could assume that in fact an infinity of straight lines exist which are all parallel to *AB* because (Figure 24) between the two limiting positions l and l' none of the straight lines going through *P* will intersect the given straight line *AB*.

We cannot properly imagine that such a thing could really happen. We instinctively assume that even the tiniest approach to the line *AB* will inevitably become proportionally greater and greater, thus bringing the two lines closer and closer together, until they must come to an intersection. But in this argumentation we make use of the "law of similarity," which says that a large figure and a small figure are exactly similar to each other, except for scale. If the law of similarity is admitted, we have already admitted the parallel postulate, since these two postulates are equivalent. If we wish, we can replace Euclid's parallel postulate by the similarity postulate. But the law of similarity is not a logical law and need not hold in the real world.

Gauss coined the name "non-Euclidean" for this class of geometries, which were first systematically investigated by the Hungarian J. Bolyai (1832) and the Russian N. Lobachevski (1826). Gauss had a very deep insight into the nature of this geometry but did not publish his results for fear of antagonizing his contemporaries, who considered any doubt in Euclid's system as plain heresy. But his later investigations concerning the nature of curved surfaces ("Disquisitiones generales circa superficies curvas," 1827) had the most profound effect on the later development of geometry, not only in relation to the geometries in which the fifth postulate of Euclid was not satisfied but in relation to the much wider group of geometries in which *none* of the Euclidean postulates are satisfied.

In the problem of geodetic surveying Gauss encountered the following problem. If we are on a plane, we can always orient ourselves in the manner of Descartes by setting up two mutually perpendicular axes and then projecting the points of the plane on these axes (Figure 25). This gives the two coordinates *x* and *y*. But on an arbitrarily curved surface we cannot draw the Cartesian system because the double system of parallel straight lines which forms the Cartesian coordinate lines does not exist. Shall that mean that it is impossible to orient ourselves on a curved surface? By no means. The Cartesian system of coordinate lines is a particularly simple and desirable method of orienting ourselves on a plane. But we can make our procedure much more flexible without destroying the basic purpose of coordinates, which is to orient ourselves on the plane and to label all the points of the plane in order to identify them. In Figure 25 on the right we have chosen two arbitrarily bent axes for our basic orientation and we have projected the point *P* on the axes *U* and *V* with the help of the curved lines *PQ* and *PR*, which do

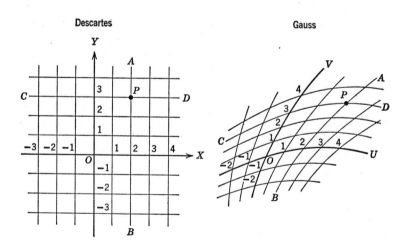

Figure 25

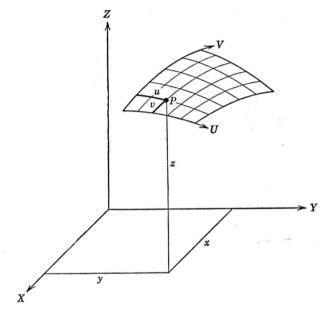

Figure 26

not follow any particular law. The purpose of the coordinates is merely to identify the point P by a pair of numbers, but this identification is possible even if our coordinate lines are arbitrarily bent lines, as long as these coordinate lines satisfy the condition that (a) the lines within each system do not intersect each other; (b) the lines of one system intersect all the lines of the other system.

A reference system of this kind, which is much more general and much more flexible than the rigid Cartesian system, is called a "Gaussian" or "curvilinear" reference system.

Before Gauss the usual method of investigating a curved surface was to operate with the three Cartesian coordinates x, y, z (Figure 26), considering the given curved surface as an entity which is imbedded in the surrounding space of three dimensions. But Gauss discovered that this surface has a life of its own. It is not necessary to go out of that surface to make geometry. We can stay *in* the surface, paying no attention to the surrounding space, and develop the "intrinsic geometry" of that surface. What is this "intrinsic geometry"?

In order to understand this term, we need the concept of the "Flatlanders." These Flatlanders are beings who live in the surface; they crawl on the surface without any notion that there exists a third dimension. We could visualize them by thinking of bugs who crawl on the surface of the earth without seeing anything that sticks out of the surface. Is it imaginable that these bugs make geometry on their surface? Indeed it is.

The fundamental elements of geometry are first of all straight lines and angles. Do we have straight lines on a curved surface? At first sight we would say *no*. The straight line between P and Q (Figure 27) is not contained in the surface S. But then we are unfair to the Flatlanders. They have a feeling of direction and say: "We can certainly walk ahead in the same direction and thus describe a straight line. And furthermore: is it not true that a straight line is the shortest communication between two points? We can stretch a string between the points P and Q, thus obtaining the line PRQ, which is our straight line." We can hardly say anything against this argument. In a similar way they can stretch a string from a fixed peg and draw a circle, or stretch a string whose ends are fixed at two points and draw an ellipse. The fact is that these Flatlanders can actually make geometry on their surface, exactly as we do it on the plane.

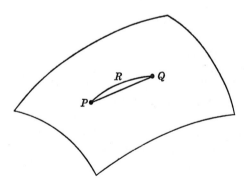

Figure 27

But then we see at once how a definite problem arises. Let us imagine that these Flatlanders live on the surface of a globe of dimensions as large as the earth. Their own dimensions are so small that they are negligible compared to the radius of the earth. These people, with their space perception restricted to a small portion of the earth, will develop a completely Euclidean world of ideas. They will say that the straight lines are infinite, that figures are freely movable, and that the law of similarity holds. The parallel postulate is included among their postulates. In every respect they will develop our ordinary Euclidean geometry. And yet they are wrong because in their world the laws of Euclidean geometry are not satisfied, for example, the sum of the angles of a triangle is not 180 degrees but larger, although the deviation is very small in triangles whose size is small compared with the radius of the earth.

This example demonstrated to Gauss that the entire Euclidean method, which starts with certain plausible but unproved postulates, may miss the real geometry realized in the physical world. Is it not possible that we may be in a similar position relative to the true laws of geometry as these Flatlanders are relative to the geometry realized on a large globe? Is there a method by which we can escape from the impasse?

Gauss found the answer. To him the Euclidean method was comparable to the procedure of Aristotle, who postulated certain properties of forces and their action on moving bodies which were wrong and thus led to a wrong form of mechanics. Galileo demolished the Aristotelian system by *measuring* and showing that these measurements demand another kind of mechanical laws. What Galileo accomplished for mechanics, Gauss accomplished for geometry. He did not want to demolish the Euclidean system but considered it imperative that one should *check* the conclusions obtained from the postulates by actual measurements. Beyond that, however, he arrived at a new foundation of geometry which dispenses with the postulates in favor of certain fundamental *measurements*, thus making geometry into a *quantitative* science, similar in character to the science of mechanics in the hands of Galileo and Newton.

Let us consider the distance $\overline{PQ}$ between two points of a curved surface (Figure 28). The ordinary distance $\overline{PQ}$ does not belong to the surface S but to the three-dimensional space in which it is imbedded. But let us now bring the point Q nearer and nearer to the point P. Then the difference between the curve PRQ and the straight line PQ diminishes more and more and if we come to a point P' which is *infinitely near* to P, the difference vanishes altogether and the straight line PP' becomes the *common property* of both space and surface. Let us then assume that we possess an *infinitesimal yardstick* with which we can measure distances between neighboring points. This distance will depend on the coordinates of the two end points P and P', but more exactly it is the *difference* of the coordinates on which this infinitesimal distance will depend. We have in higher mathematics a very definite notation for a difference (Figure 29). The difference between two x-coordinates is called Δx ("delta x"), and similarly the difference between two y-coordinates Δy. But if we have in mind *infinitesimal differences,* we change the symbol Δ to d. In our ordinary plane the distance $\overline{PP'}$ can be expressed by the Pythagorean theorem:

$$(\overline{PP'})^2 = (\Delta x)^2 + (\Delta y)^2$$

For the infinitesimal distance between two neighboring points the symbol ds has been universally adopted. Hence we write, as P and P' approach each other more and more:

$$(ds)^2 = (dx)^2 + (dy)^2$$

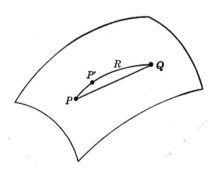

Figure 28

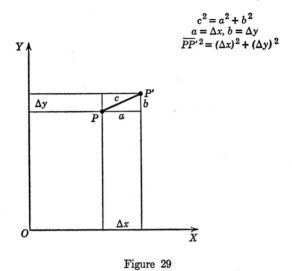

Figure 29

In a Gaussian system (Figure 30), where the coordinate lines are much less regular, we obtain the somewhat more complicated expression

$$(ds)^2 = E(du)^2 + 2F \, du \, dv + G(dv)^2$$

The three quantities E, F, G are not constants but change from point to point.

Let us now assume that we have drawn the Gaussian coordinate lines and thus labeled the points of our surface by a pair of numbers, u, v. Then we measure the three quantities E, F, G, which we can do with the help of our infinitesimal yardstick that we carry along from point to point. Then we possess at every point of the surface three fundamental quantities: E, F, G. And now the remarkable fact holds—as Gauss has demonstrated— that *the knowledge of these three quantities determines uniquely the entire intrinsic geometry of the surface* First of all, we can put these little infinitesimal lengths together and find that particular line whose length is the smallest between two fixed points. In this fashion we can define the *straight lines* (also called geodesics) of our surface. Then we can construct circles by finding

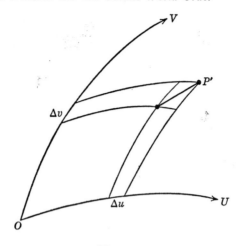

Figure 30

the locus of all points which keep the same distance from a given center C. Angles can be defined with the help of the arc length of a small circle, divided by its radius. We are thus in the possession of straight lines and angles which are the fundamental building blocks of geometry; from them all other constructions can be derived.

We see that Gauss discovered a new foundation of geometry which dispenses with the usual postulates and replaces them with three fundamental quantities which exist at every point of the surface and which are obtainable as the result of exact measurements. If the surface in question happens to be an ordinary Euclidean plane, our measurements will automatically corroborate the Euclidean postulates. For example, measuring out the three angles of a triangle we will find that the sum of the three angles gives 180 degrees. But if our surface happens to be a globe, some of the postulates of Euclid, such as the infinity of a straight line or the parallel postulate, will no longer hold. The surface in question may even be so irregular that *none* of the Euclidean postulates remain valid, but we still can measure out the surface in the Gaussian fashion, obtain the fundamental quantities E, F, G, and perform all the usual geometrical constructions. The relations between the lengths and angles of a triangle (or other geometrical relations) will then be very different from the customary relations, but our geometry will be logically just as possible as Euclid's geometry.

Gauss did not go beyond the case of two dimensions. It was B. Riemann, the ingenious pupil of Gauss, who showed how the Gaussian ideas can be generalized from two to three or any number of dimensions, thus establishing a new foundation of geometry which is not restricted to the dimension number 2. But Riemann's work cannot be imagined without the fundamental spade work of Gauss, who not only founded a new geometrical method but derived with its help a new geometrical result of exceptional beauty and far-reaching significance.

In order to characterize the curvature properties of a curved surface in the neighborhood of a point P we usually proceed in the following fashion (Figure 31). We cut the surface by planes which are laid through the normal PN and which are thus perpendicular to the tangential plane that can be drawn at the point P. There are infinitely many such planes and each one cuts out a certain curve which in the neighborhood of P can be considered as a *circle*. The radius of these circles changes as the plane swings around the normal PN. It so happens, however, that there are always two mutually perpendicular directions in which these radii attain a maximum and a minimum value. Let us call these two extreme radii R_1 and R_2. We thus speak of a minimum and a maximum curvature, given by $1/R_1$ and $1/R_2$. (We choose the *reciprocal* of the radius because the larger the circle, the smaller its curvature and vice versa.)

Now it is clear that none of these constructions have any significance for the Flatlanders for whom the normal PN does not exist since it sticks out into space and lies completely outside the given surface. Nor can they construct the plane which swings around the normal and cuts out the circles whose radius we study (called "normal sections") since these circles too are defined in relation to the three-dimensional space. Hence neither R_1 or R_2 are available without moving out of the two-dimensional world

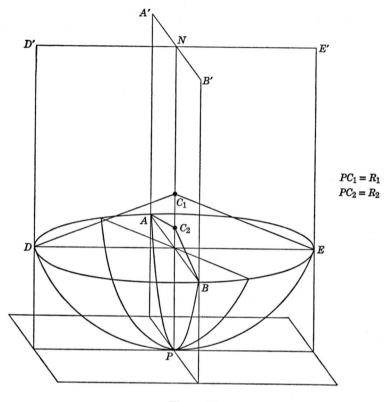

$$PC_1 = R_1$$
$$PC_2 = R_2$$

Figure 31

of the Flatlanders. The more surprising is the astonishing result
of Gauss that the *product* of these two numbers:

$$k = \frac{1}{R_1 R_2}$$

is obtainable completely on the basis of the fundamental quantities E, F, G. This means that, while the Flatlanders are unable
to imagine what the imbedding space is and what "normal sections" may mean, and what in fact a "curvature" of their surface
may mean, nevertheless the quantity k, called the "Gaussian
curvature," is *entirely available to them in terms of measurements made in the surface itself.*

Let us stop for a moment and analyze the significance of this discovery which received the name "theorema egregium," the "outstanding theorem." How do we know that the earth is a globe and not flat? All the usual proofs of this fact make use of the third dimension. We look at the stars and find the polestar at various heights above the horizon. Or we see the stacks of an approaching steamer first, because of the curvature of the earth. But let us assume that we live under a permanently cloudy sky which prevents us from making use of the third dimension and compels us to restrict our measurements to the surface of the earth. Now Gauss has shown how, with nothing but the tools of ordinary land surveying, we could deduce the fact that our earth is not flat, even though we have measured out not more than arbitrarily small portions of the earth. Moreover, these measurements would provide us with the earth's radius, if we happen to know that we have the right to assume that the two curvature radii R_1 and R_2 are equal in the case of the earth.

This curvature is a very characteristic quantity which determines the geometry realized on a certain surface. If two surfaces differ in their curvature, we know in advance that their geometries cannot agree. The Euclidean type of geometry is the simplest of all geometries in which the Gaussian curvature k is everywhere *zero*. We can now understand why the Euclidean postulates could not possess absolute significance and why the parallel postulate played such a characteristic role in the development of geometry. Even if we assume that space has everywhere the same properties and thus figures are freely movable without breaking their inner connections, this means only that the Gaussian curvature must be a *constant* at every point. But then we still have three possibilities:

$k = 0$ Euclidean geometry.

$k > 0$ spherical geometry (the geometry realized on a sphere). In this geometry the straight lines are finite (because they return on themselves) and two straight lines always intersect. In this geometry "parallel lines" do not exist.

$k < 0$ (the geometry discovered by Bolyai-Lobachevski). In

this geometry straight lines are infinite but Euclid's
parallel postulate does not hold, because from an outside point P not one but an infinity of straight lines
can be drawn which do not intersect a given straight
line.

How can we imagine that the Gaussian curvature of a surface
can become negative? In our previous figures we considered only
surfaces which were bent in one direction only. There are other
surfaces, however, which have the form of a saddle (Figure 32).
In these surfaces the two principal normal sections, which belong
to the minimum and the maximum curvatures, lie on two *opposite*
sides of P and hence have to be taken with opposite signs.
If R_1 is positive, R_2 is negative and vice versa. The product
$k = 1/R_1R_2$ comes out as a *negative* number. The "non-Euclidean geometry" of Bolyai-Lobachevski, in which straight lines are
infinite but Euclid's parallel postulate does not hold, can be realized on a surface of this kind.

Gauss also gave an exceptionally beautiful explanation of why
the intrinsic geometry of a surface is determined by the *product*
of the two principal radii R_1 and R_2, instead of R_1 and R_2 alone.
We could imagine surfaces which differ from each other as to

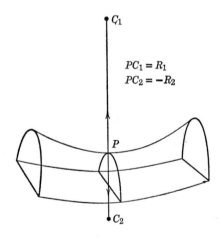

$$PC_1 = R_1$$
$$PC_2 = -R_2$$

Figure 32

R_1 and R_2, although the product R_1R_2 is in corresponding points the same. Such surfaces may look very different, yet they are related to each other by the fact that their intrinsic geometry is the same. If we gradually change the shape of a surface, while keeping the product R_1R_2 unchanged, the Flatlanders living on the surface will not notice any change. Let us imagine, for example, the Flatlanders living on a sheet of paper. We can fold this sheet into a cylinder, or a cone, or in many other shapes, without destroying in any way the mutual relations of the points of the surface. It would be different if we crumpled up the sheet and by this act destroyed the inherent geometry of its surface. But in the act of folding we respect the world of the Flatlanders, and if we watch what happens to the Gaussian coordinates of a point P, we notice that these coordinates remain unchanged, in spite of the fact that the relation of the surface to the surrounding space is changing all the time. Moreover, the infinitesimal distance between two neighboring points P and P' also remains unchanged during the act of folding. Hence the E, F, G quantities measured by the Flatlanders also do not change. But this means that the Flatlanders observe *no change* in their intrinsic geometry; in fact, the act of folding remains completely unobserved by them. The intrinsic geometry of these Flatlanders was originally the ordinary Euclidean geometry. It remains exactly the same Euclidean geometry after the deformation, although to us the surface now appears as a cylinder, or a cone, or some other more complicated surface. And in fact this is easily understandable. On the original flat sheet both the maximum and the minimum radii R_1 and R_2 were infinitely large and thus the reciprocal product $1/R_1R_2$ came out as zero. But it is enough that only *one* of the radii be infinite; this will make the product $1/R_1R_2$ zero regardless of the value of the other radius. This is the reason why an infinity of surfaces of various shapes can have the Gaussian curvature zero and thus an intrinsic geometry which is flat (Euclidean). But it would never be possible to deform this sheet of paper into a sphere. The geometry of a sphere is intrinsically different from that of a plane because its curvature has a constant positive value instead of zero. A plane sheet can be rolled into a cylinder but not into a sphere, nor can a sphere be rolled out into a plane. If the shape of the earth were cylindrical, we could make a perfect map of the earth's surface on the pages of a book. This is not possible with a globe because the Gaussian curvature of a globe and a plane do not agree. For this reason the scale of our map must change from point to point; in other words, we can only get a *distorted* picture of a globe on a plain sheet, with the result that the distances measured on the earth between various points and the corresponding distances measured on the map cannot be proportional. A distortion in mapmaking is inevitable; we can try to minimize it for the particular use to which we want to put the map, but no matter what we do a distortionless image of the earth's surface on a flat sheet is not possible.

In retrospect we can say that Gauss gave a new foundation to geometry by turning it into a *measuring* science. Although his investigations were restricted to two-dimensional spaces, he inaugurated a new way of looking at geometry which could immediately be generalized to higher dimensions. In this new method of erecting the edifice of geometry two moves are of outstanding importance. The first is that he made Descartes' rigid coordinate requirements much more flexible by getting away from the assumption of rectangular coordinates and introducing the much more general Gaussian curvilinear coordinates. When Einstein explored the possibility of breaking away from the too narrow concept of uniformly moving reference systems and changing over to arbitrarily moving reference systems, he found the answer to his search in the curvilinear coordinates of Gauss.

The second fundamental move of Gauss was the recognition that the *line element*, that is, the infinitesimal distance between two neighboring points, is a fundamental quantity on which the entire edifice of geometry may be erected. In two dimensions the line element appeared in the form

$$(ds)^2 = E(du)^2 + 2F\,du\,dv + G(dv)^2$$

which involved the three quantities E, F, and G. If these quantities were given at every point of the surface, the entire geometry of that surface would be uniquely determined. Instead of making assumptions on the basis of more or less dubious "postulates"—as Euclid did—we *measure out* our surface with the help of a small calibrated yardstick which can be carried along from point to point and which, we have to assume, does not change its length during the transportation.

The crowning achievement of the Gaussian theory was the discovery of the "curvature." Out of the fundamental quantities *E*, *F*, and *G* a single number can be constructed, the Gaussian curvature *k*, which yields a perfect characterization of the geometry of the surface. If this curvature comes out as zero at every point of the surface, the geometry becomes Euclidean and thus the entire Euclidean geometry of a plane is contained in the single statement that *k* is zero at all points. If *k* happens to be a constant at all points, the complete homogeneity of space is still preserved and figures can be moved about freely without breaking their inner connections, but the parallel postulate of Euclid (and in the case of a positive *k* also the infinity of a straight line) has to be abandoned. If *k* changes from point to point, none of the postulates of Euclid remain valid.

DISCUSSION

QUESTION. What is the significance of the Gaussian quantities *E*, *F*, and *G*, and how can they be measured?

ANSWER. The coordinate lines of a Cartesian frame of reference are particularly regular because the two axes are chosen as perpendicular to each other and we measure the *x*- and *y*-coordinates in the same units. They divide the plane into an infinity of little *squares* (Figure 33). If the axes are oblique and we measure the lengths along the *X* and *Y* axes in different units, the coordinate lines divide the plane into an infinity of little *parallelograms*. Such a parallelogram is characterized by *three* quantities: the two sides and the angle between. These three elements are in very close relation to the Gaussian *E*, *F*, and *G*. Notice that the Gaussian curvilinear coordinate lines still divide the plane into an infinity of little parallelograms but these parallelograms now *change their shape* from point to point. The essential difference between rectilinear and curvilinear coordinates is not the form of the line element but the fact that in the first case the *E*, *F*, and *G* have everywhere the *same values*, while in the second case they *change* from point to point, although in a continuous fashion. The measurement of the *E*, *F*, and *G* quantities can occur with the help of our little yard-

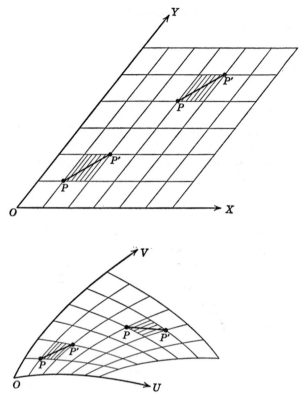

Figure 33

stick that we carry along. This yardstick puts us in a position to measure the lengths of the two sides of our little parallelograms, together with the angle between the two sides. In actuality we would not follow this theoretical procedure but would obtain the fundamental quantities by a gradual *triangulation* of the surface, analogous to the procedure used in land surveying.

5

Riemannian Geometry and Einstein's Theory of Gravitation

> *In the light of finally obtained knowledge the deductions seem almost self-evident and can be understood with no great difficulty by any intelligent student. But the foreboding search in the dark, with its intense yearnings, its alternation from confidence to despondence and then the ultimate break-through to final clarity, can only be perceived by someone who has experienced it himself.*
> EINSTEIN (1934)

THE INVESTIGATIONS of Gauss inaugurated a new era in the history of geometry. Geometry became a measuring science, in principle not so different from the science of mechanics. Gauss expressed himself in this vein in a letter to a friend, although he refrained from comments of this kind in his official publications, for fear of antagonizing the sensitivities of his contemporaries for whom the pronouncements of Euclid had an absolute and irrefutable validity. Gauss did not feel sympathetic to the Kantian view which claimed that we have the right to dictate the laws of geometry according to our own concepts, because space does not belong to the physical entities of the objective world order but is the *form* in which the substance of our sense perceptions is molded. Kant accepted the Aristotelian view which distinguishes in every kind of existence between *substance* and *form*, both together yielding the entity of a certain thing. In Kant's philosophy the *substance* of our perception of the physical world is provided by our physical sense impressions, while the *form* in which this substance manifests itself is nothing but space and time. According to this theory the laws of space and time do not belong to the physical world but are free creations of the human mind. This was Kant's attempt to find a rational explanation of the peculiar fact that the laws of geometry and the laws of algebra (so it seemed to Kant) are of an absolute and unassailable character. In Kant's time it was not yet established that there are algebras in which the laws of our ordinary algebra are not fulfilled, and also that there are geometries in which the commonly accepted postulates of geometry do not hold, without coming to any logical contradiction. Kant's theory of the absolute nature of space and time was based on the erroneous notion that "axioms" and "postulates" are of the same unassailable quality—an error which the Greeks with their cautious scientific spirit carefully avoided.

To Gauss it was clear that we have no right to dictate the laws of geometry. We can start with certain basic postulates, such as the Euclidean postulates, and then draw conclusions. But these conclusions have to be checked by careful measurements. We cannot check, for example, whether the parallel postulate of Euclid is true or not because we cannot draw lines which go out to infinity. But we can check the postulates *indirectly*, by their logical consequences. For example, a consequence of Euclid's postulates is that the sum of the three angles of a triangle equals 180 degrees. Hence by measuring the three angles of a triangle we can either verify or disprove the validity of Euclid's geometry —at least in principle since in actual fact the limited accuracy of our measurements will never allow an absolute check. Should we find that in fact the sum of the angles of a triangle is not 180 degrees, this would not mean that now the entire edifice of geometry collapses, but only that the particular system of postulates that Euclid has chosen as the basis of geometry must be abandoned in favor of some other system.

Another view, in its consequences very similar to the Kantian conclusions, was advocated by the so-called "conventionalist" school of thought, which is not far from the Machian ideas of positivism and which was particularly represented by the French mathematician Poincaré. His argument was that if we measure out a large triangle and find that its angles do not add up to 180 degrees, this does not mean that we have to give up Euclidean geometry. We could equally assume that the sides of the triangle with which we have operated are not straight but bent (Figure 34). In this fashion, of course, any deviation from the 180-degree law would become explainable. For Poincaré (and equally for the entire "positivist" school of philosophy) the problem of geometry seemed altogether irrelevant. No matter how our physical world is constructed, the ordinary Euclidean geometry would retain its validity under all circumstances because we could always project any possible deviation into the prescriptions by which we correlate a given physical situation to the world of geometry. In Poincaré's philosophy the entire idea of "understanding" the laws of the universe is not more than self-illusion. Physics can never be more than a *description* of physical events and what tools we choose for that description are immaterial, as long as we get the right answer. The selection among various theories will thus occur solely on the basis of the *simplicity* of description

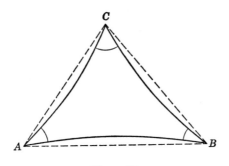

Figure 34

since it is easier to derive conclusions from simple rather than complicated formulae. Since Euclidean geometry is by far simpler than any other form of geometry, we shall retain it for the description of the physical universe and solve the difficulty of any possible deviation from the Euclidean conclusions by making the proper definitions as to the correlation of the entities of the physical world to the entities of geometry.

This "conventionalist" approach remained completely sterile. The evolution of physics accepted the Gaussian view of questioning the Euclidean postulates and testing their validity on the basis of measurements. Had Einstein accepted the idea that space and time are of no primary importance (because, no matter what world we live in, we can get along with our traditional geometry if we are only careful in correlating the given physical situation to the abstract entities of geometry), his general relativity would have remained undiscovered. But he followed an entirely different line of philosophy and his probing into the nature of gravitation led him to the inevitable conclusion that in the presence of matter our commonly accepted laws of geometry must be abandoned.

The astonishing feature of this evolution was that it suddenly reverted to an earlier phase in the history of mathematics which had remained in a dormant state for more than fifty years. The fundamentally new discoveries of Gauss did not stir the interest of his contemporaries, with the exception of his ingenious pupil, Bernhard Riemann (1826–66). He saw at once that the Gaussian discovery has tremendous possibilities because it provides a new foundation for the entire edifice of geometry. If we allow the possibility that the Euclidean postulates may be tested and possibly even disproved by measurements, would it not be more logical to start immediately with measurements and erect geometry from the beginning on a quantitative basis? Gauss has shown how the intrinsic geometry of a curved surface is completely contained in one single mathematical expression, the "line element," that is, the infinitesimal distance between two neighboring points:

$$(ds)^2 = E(du)^2 + 2F\,du\,dv + G(dv)^2$$

But why should we stop with a surface? Could we not do the same with the three-dimensional space, or indeed a space of any number of dimensions?

It was the great achievement of Riemann to show how this program could actually be accomplished. In his time there was little reason to doubt the validity of Euclidean geometry. Had not this geometry demonstrated its usefulness for thousands of years? Could anybody seriously doubt that figures are indeed freely movable in space and that space has indeed everywhere and in every direction the same properties, when our astronomical measurements yield a consistent world picture which extends to the most distant galaxies and even to nebulae which are millions of light years away?

Riemann, however, saw further than his contemporaries. He recognized the wonderful possibilities of the Gaussian "line element" and found it worthwhile to pursue this line of thought, even if it did not fit the taste of his time. In fact it is astonishing to see with what foresight he apologizes for his apparently useless investigation. He points out that some day the physicist of the future may see himself compelled to go beyond the framework of Newtonian concepts. His work has purely the purpose of clearing the way to a broader approach so that, when that time comes, science should not be hamstrung by traditional prejudices. No words could have expressed more adequately the historical destiny which was in store for Einstein.

Riemann's prophetic utterance was spoken at the end of his "inaugural address," given on the occasion of his election to the mathematical faculty of the University of Goettingen (1854). It was purely accidental that this magnificent lecture of Riemann came into being. The candidate had to suggest three topics and usually the head of the department accepted the first suggestion as the topic of discussion. But on this occasion Gauss found the third topic, entitled: "On the hypotheses which are at the foundation of geometry," particularly to his taste. Riemann's lecture gave a general nontechnical summary of his fundamental investigation of a class of geometries, now called "Riemannian geometries," which are based on the existence of a line element, that is, the infinitesimal distance between any two neighboring points.

In this work Riemann extended the Gaussian method of erecting the intrinsic geometry of a curved surface solely on the line element, generalizing this idea from two to an arbitrary number of dimensions. In the course of these investigations he discovered the deeper implications of that Gaussian "curvature," which was not more than a mere number in the Gaussian theory of curved surfaces.

Yet this great structure of ingenious mathematical deductions was so much out of harmony with the historical period that it was not published in Riemann's lifetime and came to the attention of the world only posthumously. However, considering all the given circumstances, this peculiar oversight on the part of Riemann's contemporaries is not so surprising. The people primarily interested in geometry like to see things in space; they like to draw figures such as triangles, quadrangles, circles, ellipses, and so on, and base their conclusions on the visible symmetry properties of space. In Riemann's geometry no figures are drawn, no constructions are made, everything follows by the abstract tools of analysis. This kind of geometry did not appeal to Riemann's contemporaries, particularly since they could see no compelling reason to give up the much simpler Euclidean foundation of geometry in favor of a geometry which seemed so much more brittle and less manageable. To this it must be added that the proper mathematical tool for the adequate study of Riemannian geometry, now called "absolute calculus" or "tensor calculus," did not yet exist in Riemann's time. Hence the proper understanding of the importance of Riemann's far-reaching ideas was hardly possible in those days.

Actually, the symmetry elements of space come to expression even in Riemann's geometry, but on a more abstract level. There is a crystal-like beauty in the constructions of Riemannian geometry but it demanded a language of its own. The Gaussian notation u, v, for the generalized coordinates of a point in the plane and the expression

$$(ds)^2 = E\,(du)^2 + 2F\,du\,dv + G\,(dv)^2$$

for the line element would be entirely unsuitable for a successful investigation of the properties of this peculiar form of geometry.

In mathematics the question of *structure* is of supreme importance and we can make no headway whatever if our notations do not harmonize with the structure we want to investigate. Riemann noticed that the first requirement is that we should recognize the proper structure of the line element. For this purpose the introduction of the *subscript notation* is of paramount importance. Let us assume that we consider the children born to Mr. Smith. The family name Smith is then applied to all the children and the individual children will be distinguished by first names such as Richard, Robert, Barbara, Peter, and so on. These names have obviously no functional significance. In mathematics we prefer to use a different kind of labelling system:

$$S_1, S_2, S_3, \ldots$$

The "subscript" 1, 2, 3, . . . brings immediately into evidence the sequence in which the children were born, S_1 referring to the first, S_2 to the second, S_3 to the third child of Mr. Smith. We could go further and differentiate between boys and girls by the prefixed signs $+$ and $-$ (or vice versa, according to taste). Our analogy is lame in an important respect, inasmuch as in mathematics we do not operate with persons or any other kind of entities but solely with *quantities* which can be characterized by definite *numbers*.

We can go further and use a similar notation for the children of the next generation. Accordingly the first child of S_1 will be denoted S_{11}, the second S_{12}, the third S_{13}, and so on. Hence S_{13} will denote the third child of Mr. Smith's first child, while S_{31} refers to the first child of Mr. Smith's third child, and so on. The third generation will then demand *three* subscripts, such as S_{111}, S_{112}, and so on (read "S sub one one one," or briefly "S one one one," etc.), the fourth generation four subscripts, and so forth. In mathematics the various members belonging to the same generation are called "components" and the entire assembly of such a generation is called a "tensor." Instead of the "first, second, third, fourth generation," we speak of a "tensor of the first, second, third, fourth order."

The coordinates by which we characterize the position of a point of space should obviously be considered as members of one family and accordingly denoted by the subscript method. Instead of calling the Gaussian coordinates u, v, we will thus prefer to use the notation x_1, x_2. Similarly, in order to understand the structure of the line element, we will no longer write it in terms of E, F, and G, but will introduce the following functional notation:

$$(ds)^2 = g_{11}(dx_1)^2 + g_{12}\, dx_1\, dx_2 + g_{21}\, dx_2\, dx_1 + g_{22}(dx_2)^2$$

The notation g_{11} instead of E has the great advantage that it immediately indicates that it belongs to the product $dx_1\, dx_1 = (dx_1)^2$; the notation g_{12} instead of F immediately indicates that it belongs to the product $dx_1\, dx_2$, and so on. Hence the new notation has functional and structural value, which was not the case with the Gaussian notation E, F, and G. Moreover, the above arrangement indicates that we should write down the basic quantities, or "components," of the Gaussian line element in the arrangement of a chessboard:

g_{11}	g_{12}
g_{21}	g_{22}

Actually, we could combine the two terms $g_{12}\, dx_1\, dx_2$ and $g_{21}\, dx_2\, dx_1$ into one instead of considering them separately. But by doing so we would lose the proper understanding for the structure of the line element which demands that we should keep g_{12} and g_{21} as separate entities, although they agree in value:

$$g_{12} = g_{21}$$

This reduces the four g-quantities from four to three different numbers.

If Mr. Smith has two children and every child in turn has two children, and so on, the successive generations will increase like powers of two:

$$2, 4, 8, 16, \ldots$$

If Mr. Smith has three children and once more the scheme continues, the successive generations will increase in powers of three:

$$3, 9, 27, 81, \ldots$$

If every generation comprises four children, the successive generations will increase in powers of four:

$$4, 16, 64, 256, \ldots$$

Hence we see that the number of components of a tensor of a higher order can become quite large.

Let us consider as an example the Riemannian geometry of a space of three dimensions. Here we need three Gaussian coordinates for the characterization of the point P in space:

$$x_1, x_2, x_3.$$

The line element, that is, the infinitesimal distance between P and the neighboring point P', can now be written down as follows:

$$(\overline{PP'})^2 = (ds)^2 = g_{11}(dx_1)^2 + g_{12}\, dx_1\, dx_2 + g_{13}\, dx_1\, dx_3$$
$$+ g_{21}\, dx_2\, dx_1 + g_{22}(dx_2)^2 + g_{23}\, dx_2\, dx_3$$
$$+ g_{31}\, dx_3\, dx_1 + g_{32}\, dx_3\, dx_2 + g_{33}(dx_3)^2$$

The g-quantities form the components of a "tensor of second order," called the "metrical tensor." Once more we can arrange these components in a chessboard scheme which is now a 3 by 3 board:

g_{11}	g_{12}	g_{13}
g_{21}	g_{22}	g_{23}
g_{31}	g_{32}	g_{33}

These nine quantities represent in fact only six different numbers, on account of the symmetry relations

$$g_{12} = g_{21}, \quad g_{13} = g_{31}, \quad g_{23} = g_{32}$$

We could imagine that by placing a mirror along the diagonal of our chessboard we can make the corresponding components above and below the diagonal equal to each other. A tensor of this kind is called a "symmetric tensor of second order."

Finally we come to the four-dimensional space-time world, characterized by the four Gaussian coordinates

$$x_1, x_2, x_3, x_4,$$

which take the place of our previous x, y, z, t. If we write down once more the fundamental line element—which contains the entire geometry of the physical world—we now obtain a chess-board scheme of four rows and four columns:

$$(ds)^2 = g_{11}(dx_1)^2 + g_{12}\, dx_1\, dx_2 + g_{13}\, dx_1\, dx_3 + g_{14}\, dx_1\, dx_4$$

$$+ g_{21}\, dx_2\, dx_1 + g_{22}(dx_2)^2 + g_{23}\, dx_2\, dx_3 + g_{24}\, dx_2\, dx_4$$

$$+ g_{31}\, dx_3\, dx_1 + g_{32}\, dx_3\, dx_2 + g_{33}(dx_3)^2 + g_{34}\, dx_3\, dx_4$$

$$+ g_{41}\, dx_4\, dx_1 + g_{42}\, dx_4\, dx_2 + g_{43}\, dx_4\, dx_3 + g_{44}(dx_4)^2$$

g_{11}	g_{12}	g_{13}	g_{14}
g_{21}	g_{22}	g_{23}	g_{24}
g_{31}	g_{32}	g_{33}	g_{34}
g_{41}	g_{42}	g_{43}	g_{44}

$$g_{12} = g_{21}$$
$$g_{13} = g_{31}$$
$$g_{14} = g_{41}$$
$$g_{23} = g_{32}$$
$$g_{24} = g_{42}$$
$$g_{34} = g_{43}$$

Once more the mirror scheme operates, cutting down the original sixteen components to only ten different components. The entire geometry of the space-time world is thus characterized by ten quantities which will generally not be constants but will change from point to point, thus forming what we call in physics a "field."

Now we have seen that Gauss was able to characterize the entire intrinsic geometry of a curved surface by one single quantity, k, called the "Gaussian curvature." If this quantity is zero, we are immediately back at the geometry of Euclid. Riemann asked himself, what will correspond to this quantity in more than two dimensions? How can we tell from a given line element whether the geometry established by it is of the Euclidean kind or not? He made the fundamental discovery that the decisive quantity is far from a single number but is in fact a *tensor of fourth order*. This means that we have to go up to the *fourth generation* in order to find the decisive quantity which characterizes the nature of our geometry. If all components of this tensor vanish, we are back at Euclid's flat geometry. But if even one component happens to be different from zero, our geometry is no longer Euclidean; there exists a certain "curvature" in our world.

But then, if we have to go to as high as four generations to obtain the characteristic quantity of our geometry, will that not lead to a tremendously heavy machinery? Did we not find that the fourth generation will contain in two dimensions 16, in three dimensions 81, and in four dimensions 256 components? In actual fact the number of components can be greatly reduced if the tensor possesses certain symmetry properties; this is actually the case with the Riemann tensor. In the language of the previous analogy we may say that in the successive generations some of the children may be stillborn and in addition we may have a number of identical twins whom we will not count separately.

Let us consider for example the component R_{1212} (the symbol R is chosen in honor of Riemann). We focus our attention on the first two subscripts. Then the following symmetry law holds:

$$R_{1212} = -R_{2112}$$

that is, *an exchange of two subscripts yields the same value but with an opposite sign.* If we apply this law to the component R_{1112} we obtain

$$R_{1112} = -R_{1112}$$

But no number can be equal to its own negative, unless the number is *zero.* Hence all components which start with two equal subscripts are immediately zero. Furthermore, the previous symmetry property holds not only with respect to the first pair of subscripts but also with respect to the second pair:

$$R_{1212} = -R_{1221}$$

Hence all components are equally zero in which the second pair of subscripts take the same value.

But then, let us examine the case of two dimensions, in which the subscripts can assume only two values: 1 and 2. Here we see that the only component which really counts is the single component

$$R_{1212}$$

because all the other components are either zero or reducible to this one component. For example, $R_{2112} = -R_{1212}$, and thus does not count as a new component. We thus see that in two dimensions the characteristic curvature quantity of a Riemannian geometry is reducible to *one single number,* and we now understand how Gauss could characterize the intrinsic geometry of a curved surface (which represents a Riemannian geometry of two dimensions) by one single quantity, the Gaussian curvature k.

We now come to the case of three dimensions (that is, our ordinary space, if time is omitted). Here we obtain the following scheme of subscript combinations, if we omit all combinations which are either zero or a duplication of something we already have.

$$
\begin{array}{ccc}
12\ 12, & 12\ 13, & 12\ 23 \\
13\ 12, & 13\ 13, & 13\ 23 \\
23\ 12, & 23\ 13, & 23\ 23
\end{array}
$$

These are altogether *nine* quantities. In actual fact this number is reduced to *six* because our previous mirror scheme comes once more into operation. This is caused by a further symmetry property of the Riemann tensor, that *an exchange of the first subscript pair with the second makes no change in the value of the curvature component.* Hence in the end only six independent components remain which we can arrange as follows:

$$
\begin{array}{ccc}
R_{1212}, & R_{1213}, & R_{1223} \\
& R_{1313}, & R_{1323} \\
& & R_{2323}
\end{array}
$$

The number 81 has been reduced to 6.

Finally we come to the four-dimensional world of the physical universe. Here our subscript scheme becomes, omitting all duplications,

12 12	12 13	12 14	12 23	12 24	12 34
	13 13	13 14	13 23	13 24	13 34
		14 14	14 23	14 24	14 34
			23 23	23 24	23 34
				24 24	24 34
					34 34

This means altogether 21 independent components, but this number is reduced to 20 by one further symmetry property of the Riemann tensor which demands four different subscripts for its operation and thus did not appear in either two or three dimensions. Because of this symmetry law we obtain the relation

$$R_{1234} + R_{1342} + R_{1423} = 0$$

which establishes a relation between the three underlined components and makes only two of them independent. We see that the symmetry properties of the Riemann tensor are such that in four dimensions the total number of independent components is reduced from 256 to 20.

All this was done by Riemann himself. Much later the mathematician Christoffel rediscovered the Riemann tensor, which is thus frequently referred to as the "Riemann-Christoffel tensor." But nothing essentially new was added to Riemann's original work, nor was any serious attempt made to apply these ideas to the world of physics. In fact, there was not the slightest motivation to think that for the description of physical reality something like a curved geometry would be demanded. More astonishing even than the final accomplishment was the road that led Einstein to Riemannian geometry, which, recovered from history and viewed from the light of theoretical physics, was used to reach one of the most dazzling discoveries of the human mind.

Einstein's approach was not the demand for aesthetic or philosophical satisfaction, which dominated so much the final achievement. His starting point was a very concrete physical problem and it was only after the erection of the entire edifice that he became aware of the wonderful wisdom which seems to permeate the universe. Einstein's starting point was simple enough. He did not feel satisfied with the accomplishment of special relativity which has put all reference systems moving relative to each other with constant velocity on an equal footing. Why should not *all* reference systems be put on an equal footing? In his search for an answer to this problem he naturally came across first of all the uniformly *accelerated* reference systems, as the first group of systems which were not included in the legitimate group of systems of his theory of 1905. If we want to go beyond the re-

stricted class of uniformly moving systems, the first generalization is the assumption that two systems move relative to each
other with constant *acceleration*. What can we say about such
systems? He noticed at once that such systems must have something to do with the phenomenon of *gravitation*.

Let us assume that we are in one of the usual "legitimate" reference systems permitted by special relativity. We imagine that
we are somewhere out in empty space, infinitely far from all
masses so that the gravitational force is practically zero in our
system. Hence the bodies have no weight, water does not pour
out of a glass, a pendulum clock does not move, and all the other
consequences of a completely weightless state are realized. We
imagine a physicist enclosed in his laboratory at this point of the
universe. Now a peculiar thing happens. A giant begins to pull
his laboratory upward with the uniform acceleration of 32 feet
per second squared, and a peculiar transformation takes place.
Suddenly everything occurs exactly as we are wont to observe
on earth. The pendulum clock swings and shows the time in
the usual way, a stone released falls with the usual acceleration
of 32 feet per second squared, water pours out of the glass in the
customary fashion, and so on. The physicist makes his measurements and finds everything in perfect harmony with the usual
phenomena which occur in a uniform gravitational field. He
thinks that he is on earth, under the influence of the gravitational force of the earth. He has no idea that in fact there is no
gravitational force at all, but that a giant is pulling his laboratory upward. The fact that he is in a uniformly accelerated reference system *imitates completely the behavior of a uniform
gravitational field.* This is the celebrated "equivalence hypothesis" of Einstein which asserts that everything we observe in a
uniform field of gravity can be imitated by putting ourselves into
an accelerated frame of reference. Let us observe that this
equivalence idea is possible only if it is true that all masses fall
in a field of gravity with exactly the same acceleration, in other
words, that the heavy (gravitational) mass of a body is strictly
proportional to its inertial mass. That this is so was demonstrated to an uncanny degree by the exact measurements of the
Hungarian physicist L. Eötvös (1890).

Two important consequences can be drawn from this equivalence principle. The fact that the force of gravity did not exist in our original reference system but came into existence solely through its motion suggests that perhaps the "force of gravity" is no real force at all but an "apparent force" of the same kind as the centrifugal force on earth which comes into existence solely because the earth rotates around its axis. All apparent forces are strictly proportional to the inertial mass of the moving body, and the puzzling and quite mysterious property of the Newtonian force of gravity, to be always strictly proportional to the inertial mass, would find its natural explanation if the "gravitational force," as such, were to disappear and be replaced by an "apparent force" which acts in that particular reference system. The physical phenomena observed within the capsule of an astronaut in orbit fully corroborate Einstein's contention. In the reference system of the astronaut the force of gravity is nonexistent. This force comes into existence only if we describe the motion of the astronaut from a reference system located on earth.

The second observation of Einstein had even more decisive consequences. He assumed that the equivalence of a uniform gravitational field and a uniformly accelerated frame of reference is of *universal* significance, an all-comprehensive *principle* of nature, which holds with respect to *all* physical phenomena. In that case we can find out what happens in a uniform field of gravity by observing the phenomena which occur in a uniformly accelerated frame of reference. Let us now imagine that we observe a light ray which propagates horizontally while we are pulled upward. We would observe that this light ray no longer pursues a straight path but is bent downward, as if light itself were subjected to the gravitational attraction of the earth. But if that is so, the second postulate of the relativity theory of 1905, namely, that light travels in every direction with the same uniform speed, cannot hold in the presence of a field of gravity. The relativity theory of 1905 has to be restricted to those domains of the universe in which the field of gravitation is negligible. In the presence of any field of gravity the relativity postulate of 1905 can no longer hold. Light velocity is no longer an absolute constant of nature. But if this is so, we see at once that the geometry of the space-time world is put in jeopardy. As Min-kowski has shown, the constancy of light velocity is equivalent to the assumption that the space-time world possesses a metrical structure which is of the extended Euclidean kind, that is, whose curvature is zero. This can no longer be true if we take into account the existence of universal gravitation which destroys the constancy of light velocity. But what happens then in the pres-ence of a gravitational field? We must abandon the hypothesis of a flat Euclidean world. And what must we put in its place? We must generalize the geometry of the space-time world to a more general structure and we can hope that this structure will reveal something of the true nature of gravitation.

To this must be added Einstein's desire to get away from the privileged position of uniformly moving frames of reference in favor of systems which can be in an arbitrary state of motion. Here Einstein's friend Marcel Grossmann came to his aid. Gross-mann acquainted him with the properties of Gaussian coordi-nates, in which the too rigid requirements of the Cartesian axes were overcome and a very great generalization of the coordinate concept achieved. It became clear to Einstein that the solution of his problem had to come through the use of the Gaussian co-ordinates.

As the next step forward he noticed that in all formulae of absolute calculus or tensor calculus—which has as its aim the formulation of the laws of physics in arbitrary coordinates—a peculiar quantity appeared which had remained hidden in operat-ing with the Cartesian kind of coordinates. This quantity was the "metrical tensor" g with its ten components, exactly the same tensor which formed the components of the Gaussian line element. It seemed that this metrical tensor has to be added to the other physical field quantities as an equal partner. This meant that one had to find certain determining equations, called "field equa-tions," for its characterization. From where should we take these field equations?

We could make use of Riemann's curvature tensor and say that this tensor must vanish. Then we would be back at the flat world of Minkowski. But let us examine this statement more carefully. In four dimensions the metrical tensor g had *ten* different components. On the other hand, the tensor R of Riemann had *twenty* different components. If we say that the Riemann curvature tensor vanishes, we demand *twenty* equations of only *ten* quantities. This is obviously not reasonable. We demand too much. We overdetermine our system. *Ten* quantities should not satisfy more than *ten* equations. Somehow we should reduce the twenty components of the Riemann tensor to only ten components. This was indeed possible by a routine operation of tensor calculus, called "contraction." This "contracted curvature tensor" could be considered as a true characterization of our metrical geometry. Let us take this tensor and put it equal to zero. This now yields a well-balanced system of equations: ten equations for ten quantities.

The examination of these equations led to sensational results. Ten equations of a very complicated structure for ten quantities appears at first sight as a hopelessly difficult mathematical problem. But fortunately, applied to the solar system, some great simplifications take place. First of all, nature does us the favor that even the greatest masses make only a very slight indention on the flat Euclidean world of Minkowski. Hence we can assume that the deviations from a Euclidean metric are very small. And second, in the solar system we have a central body, the sun, whose mass is overwhelmingly greater than the masses of the surrounding planets. Hence we could assume the presence of one single mass only and, furthermore, in view of the spherical shape of the sun we could assume that this mass creates a field which is characterized by complete symmetry, in whatever direction we may proceed from the center of the sun.

Under these conditions a great simplification took place and the ten components of the metrical tensor could be expressed in terms of *one single component*. It thus becomes explicable why Newton in his much simpler theory succeeded in describing gravitation with the help of one function only, the "gravitational potential." The remaining function in Einstein's theory followed almost the same law as Newton's potential. In addition, the assumption of a special "gravitational force" became superfluous. The planets revolved around the sun, not because they were acted upon by a force of gravity but because they moved under their own inertia. They merely described *straight lines* of the space-time world. But how could the closed ellipses of the planetary orbits be straight lines? They were actually straight lines, but ones that belonged to a Riemannian world, created by the mass of the sun, and not a flat Euclidean world, void of all masses. The masses are the real agents which determine the geometry of the world. Without masses the world would have the flat structure of the Minkowskian geometry. With masses the world has the curved structure of a Riemannian geometry.

Another tremendous eye-opener was the realization that a slight modification of the contracted curvature tensor introduced by Einstein automatically satisfied the conservation laws of energy and momentum which are among the most fundamental principal properties of all matter. Hence one could explain why in all physical phenomena the fundamental conservation laws are encountered, which hold without exception. The reason is that physical matter is suddenly resolved into a purely geometrical entity, the curvature tensor of Einstein, which has by the very nature of Riemannian geometry the property of satisfying the conservation laws. If special relativity has shown that time is nothing but a fourth coordinate in a unified geometrical structure including space and time, now general relativity has shown that this geometrical structure is still more comprehensive by including not only space and time, but even *matter*, because matter can be interpreted as a certain curved portion of space. Space, time, and matter became united into one single and inseparable structure which includes the entire physical world. While before "time" could be measured in centimeters, now also "matter" could be measured in centimeters. Geometry became the fundamental entity which included all existence.

When Einstein finished his calculations, an almost unbelievable result emerged which vindicated his struggles beyond all expectations. The Newtonian theory gave a very excellent close approximation of the solutions of Einstein's field equations. But by going one step further and obtaining a still closer approximation, a very slight deviation from the Newtonian theory came in sight. The planetary orbits did not close exactly. A planet did not return after one revolution exactly to the same spot where it stood one revolution earlier, but advanced by a very small amount. The ellipse in which the planet revolves around the sun is not completely stationary but is in itself in a very slow revolution in its own plane. The major axis of the planetary orbit moves very slowly forward in the plane of revolution, in the same direction in which the planet revolves around the sun. We thus speak of an "advance" of the major axis. This advance becomes a maximum in the case of the nearest planet, Mercury, but even there the effect is very minute. It takes *three million years* for the major axis of the Mercury orbit to make one complete revolution around the sun. Although the effect is very small, it is nevertheless measurable, in view of the great accuracy of astronomical measurements and the fact that the observations of hundreds of years are at our disposal. The advance of the Mercury perihelion was actually known to astronomers for more than a hundred years, due to the very careful calculations of the French astronomer Leverrier. The amount of the advance agreed exactly with the prediction made by Einstein's gravitational theory. The tremendous consistency which permeates creation was thus demonstrated on a magnificent scale.

An optical effect, measurable only on the occasion of a total eclipse of the sun, was also tested in 1919 by an expedition of English astronomers. The experimental results were again in full agreement with the predictions of the theory.

That Einstein became world famous overnight is understandable but not of primary importance. The truly sensational part of the theory was not that it predicted some small effects which went beyond the boundaries of the Newtonian theory. In our strongly pragmatically oriented century all that counts is success and the value of a theory is measured by verification of the predictions it makes. Had Einstein's theory merely corroborated Newton's theory without predicting any new effects, the intellectual achievement would have been exactly the same but Einstein would have failed to make the mark in the professional evaluation of his colleagues. If we can describe gravitation in the simple Newtonian terms, why should we choose the incomparably more complicated Einsteinian theory?

This astonishingly short-sighted scientific philosophy misses completely the true significance of Einstein's incomparable discovery. "All we have to do is to describe the observed phenomena"—this is the slogan of the Mach-Poincaré type of positivistic philosophy. Find a mathematical equation which fits the observation and your work as a mathematical physicist is done. Never ask the question whether one can understand something or not; there is no such thing as "understanding," there is only "describing."

With Einstein's achievement the sober assertions of the positivists are left a million miles behind. To find a mathematical equation which fits the phenomena means nothing. The form of the mathematical law is scrutinized and its deeper substance discovered. The law is not accidentally *this* law which could also be some *other* law. The law is the consequence of some sweeping and universal *principles* which act in the universe and which demonstrate the intrinsic wisdom that permeates all creation. "It must be so," is the new slogan, not "it is so." Einstein's incomparable genius has demonstrated how constructive mathematical thinking, combined with philosophical and artistic imagination, can climb to heights which were never possible before and perhaps will never be surpassed. The one-ness of the universe and its inherent inevitableness were demonstrated by the most exact mathematical reasoning.

DISCUSSION

QUESTION. Is Einstein's general relativity universally accepted?

ANSWER. It is difficult to answer this question since no theory is universally accepted. There are always some cranks who propose "theories" off the beaten track. Such "theories" are usually not taken seriously. In the case of Einstein, however, even intellectuals of high standing have tried their hands at offering rival theories. Taking a little Newton, a little Minkowski, a little Einstein, and mixing them in various proportions, the concoction is offered as a new theory of gravitation. An amusing feature of these theories is that they are always eager to include the three so-called "relativistic effects"—the perihelion advance, the bending of light rays, and the red shift of the spectral lines—in order to balance the spectacular features of Einstein's gravitational theory (thus colliding with some other anti-Einstein fanatics who claim that the optical predictions are plain hoax, disproved by the actual observations). Einstein commented on these efforts in his usual humorous fashion which was free of all malice: "Sin remains sin, even if committed by otherwise respectable people." The great advantage of these theories is that they are belabored and artificial, thus lacking the logical directness and inherent necessity of Einstein's thought constructions. In this manner they satisfy the positivistic program which denies to the human intellect the right to speculate and abhors everything that smacks of "a priori" thinking. But if we look at these theories detached from the human scene and ask the question: "Who represents the cosmic spirit, Einstein or his adversaries?"—can there be doubt where the answer lies?

QUESTION. Can we consider Einstein's theory as the final word in gravitation?

ANSWER. Nothing is final in science, but we can make a few cautious predictions. Science will never go back to the old Newtonian ideas of an absolute space and an absolute time. The relativistic unification of space and time is today the best verified theory in all physics. General relativity is in a less settled state. Einstein himself did not stop with his theory of 1916 but continued to work on further extensions of the geometrical interpretation of physical phenomena. Although gravitation is a relatively minor phenomenon in comparison to the electric and quantum phonomena, we can hardly hope to have obtained a complete understanding of the essence of gravitation before we have found that truly "unified field theory" on which Einstein worked during the last years of his life, without coming to a truly satisfactory solution.

QUESTION. What was Einstein's opinion concerning cosmological speculations?

ANSWER. Shortly after the discovery of general relativity Einstein was engaged in cosmological ideas. He noticed that general relativity gave a new basis for a successful resolution of some of the puzzling problems of the world at large. Euclidean space is infinite and this represents a very great handicap from the standpoint of physics. To imagine that all matter extends to infinity—thus making the energy content of the universe infinitely large—is both physically and philosophically hard to accept. On the other hand, if matter is finite (and thus the number of stars and galaxies also finite), an equilibrium between the finite matter and the infinite space cannot be achieved. Einstein's gravitational theory has shown that the distribution of matter throughout space establishes an average curvature which bends the flat Euclidean space into a space of spherical structure in which the element of infinity is excluded because the straight lines return into themselves and are thus of

finite extension. A space of this type solves all the previously un-
solvable problems of Newtonian physics concerning a reasonable
relation between matter at large and space.

In later years, however, Einstein did not return to the cosmological problem, except in brief remarks. The reason is quite understandable. How can we make statements as to happenings in immense distances when we do not yet understand the structure of
even the tiniest atom? The nature of electricity, the quantum
phenomena, atomism—these are the real problems of science which
have not yet been answered in a satisfactory manner. As long as
we do not have a unified view which would include all the basic
phenomena of the physical world, cosmological speculations are idle
and endowed with a certain arrogance to which we are not entitled.
Einstein was always opposed to an exploitation of science for sensational purposes and to the pretense to know when in fact we do
not know. He could allow himself the rare privilege of modesty
which says: "I do not know."

Once Nernst, the great physicochemist, pondering on the great
quandary of the physical sciences that all energy forms of nature
seem to be converted eventually into heat and that the universe is
aging more and more without visible signs of rejuvenation, con-
cocted an ingenious scheme which allowed a reconversion of heat
into matter and thus made a periodic universe possible in which
the beginning and end of time was eliminated. In his enthusiasm
he called up Einstein (with whom he had the best of scientific and
the worst of personal relations; the personalities of these two great
men of science were utterly clashing) and explained to him how he
envisaged the evolution of the world over billions of years, asking
his opinion about this theory. Einstein's comment was: "I was not
present."

6

Summary and Outlook

*To someone who could grasp the universe from one unified view-
point, the entire creation would appear as a unique fact and a
great truth.*

J. D'ALEMBERT (1751)

WE HAVE TRAVELED a considerable distance since the beginning
of our discussions. The time has come for a résumé and integrated evaluation of the new world of ideas which was inaugurated by Einstein's achievements. The twenty years between
1905 and 1925 saw a revolution in our traditional way of thinking, unprecedented in the entire history of science. And this
revolution was almost singlehandedly the work of one man:
Albert Einstein.

The beginnings were not particularly startling. A paper published in the *Annalen der Physik* had the title: "On the electro-
dynamics of moving bodies." On the surface it dealt with some
specific properties of optical and electromagnetic phenomena
which were now presented in novel fashion. In actual fact it
presented an entirely new approach to our most ingrained fundamental ideas concerning the structure of the physical world: the
concepts of space and time. The idea of an absolute space and
an absolute time, which was at the foundation of Newtonian
physics, was shown to be untenable in the face of certain unde-
niable experimental evidence. A new foundation of physics was

demanded which harmonized with the results of the experiments.

The novel feature in Einstein's approach was that where other people saw an isolated event, he recognized the operation of fundamental principles. This feature of his early papers of 1905 remained a characteristic feature of his entire scientific career. Other physicists explained the same phenomena that Einstein explained, but he saw deeper than the others because for him the universe was an integrated whole in which all-pervasive principles were at work. And thus every one of his discoveries was of principal significance. This put him more in the category of a philosopher than of a specialist who sees things with professional eyes.

The principle of the equal admissibility of all reference systems in uniform motion relative to each other (special relativity); the principle of the equivalence of mass and energy; the principle of the equivalence of a gravitational field with an accelerated frame of reference; the principle of the equal admissibility of arbitrary reference systems (general relativity)—these are landmarks in the history of physics, which before had recognized the operation of *laws* but now recognized the operation of interconnecting *principles*. Planck explained his radiation law by assuming that energy is not radiated out continuously but in definite discrete bundles, called "quanta." No, said Einstein, this is not enough. Something much deeper is here at work. The difference between particle and wave breaks down. Certain phenomena of light emission can be understood only if we conceive of light as a particle which moves with light velocity. This was the concept of the "light quanta" (now called "photons")—a radical departure from our earlier concepts.

This kind of thinking was completely new in the annals of science, and the early antagonism of the physicists toward Einstein's way of seeing things is easily understandable. Where Einstein saw that the concepts of space and time were involved and demanded modification, they wanted an explanation in terms of physical concepts. And thus they complained that Einstein did not solve the problem but hid it in a maze of mathematical formulae. For them Einstein's special relativity was not a physical theory but a clever conjuring trick of mathematical magic.

But then Minkowski came and demonstrated that Einstein's theory in fact allows no strictly physical interpretation because it is equivalent to a new foundation of geometry in which space and time are no longer independent categories, but merely two different aspects of a unified space-time world in which a unified geometry was at work. Newton's absolute space and absolute time were abandoned in favor of an absolute four-dimensional world, the world of space-time.

To get used to this much more abstract way of thinking was not easy. In an early meeting on relativity one of the participants walked out in anger with the remark: "I am a physicist, not a mathematician." Somewhat later another participant walked out in anger, saying: "I am a physicist, not a philosopher." The idea that there are watertight compartments into which we put our concepts was repugnant to Einstein, who saw the world as an integrated whole, without sharp boundaries between the various branches of science. In the earlier phases of physics, one thought in predominantly physical pictures rather than in abstract mathematical formulations. Mathematics was tolerated as a kind of necessary evil, but the demands on the advanced tools of mathematics were rather modest. With the development of both relativity and quantum theory the shift toward abstract thinking became very pronounced. We no longer believe that physical action is explainable in terms of little hard balls which are the centers of all kinds of forces. A much more abstract kind of concept is demanded in which the particle is no longer something that can be considered in isolation but rather as a part of an all-embracing entity, called a "field." In this development Einstein's thought constructions played a vital role.

When Minkowski in 1908 demonstrated that Einstein's new theory was equivalent to a new geometrical approach uniting space and time in one single entity, the voices for a "physical" explanation of relativity fell silent, since it now became obvious that an explanation in physical terms cannot be given. Special relativity was a geometrical, not a physical, phenomenon and thus the explanation had to be given in the language of geometry and not in the language of physics. But this was only the beginning. In a few years time the mathematization of physics became even more pronounced, when Einstein began to speculate on the nature of gravitation. Here the heavy apparatus of tensor calculus had to be invoked and finally a theory evolved which in speculative boldness surpassed everything that ever existed in the realm of physical thought. The problem of geometry now came into the center of discussion and a new foundation of geometry was the result, a geometry in which the geometry realized in nature became amalgamated with the physical properties of matter. If before, time was absorbed by space, now matter became absorbed by space, giving us a new physical world picture in which matter appeared as a certain curvature property of the space-time world.

This gradual abstractization of our primitive concepts may appear on the surface as a loss. We can regret the fact that so many of our cherished ideas concerning space, time and matter had to be thrown overboard. How simple was the picture of the physical world before Einstein's relativity and quantum theory appeared on the scene. We could go a long way with the simple concepts of force, work, energy, and a few similar ideas. Today the picture of the physical world is infinitely more complex. Where Newton succeeded with one single quantity, Einstein introduced *ten* quantities and the relations between these quantities is by far more complex than the simple equation found by Newton. Should we not deplore then the passing of the naive phase of physics, comparable to the golden age of mankind, spent in a paradisiac innocence of fairy tales? Today, from the perspective of history, the evolution from Newton to Einstein appears to us in a different light. We admit the loss of simplicity, but we are willing to pay the price for the sake of the tremendous advance in *unity*. It is the wisdom of cosmic events which came so eminently in the foreground through the work of Einstein. In the early years of relativity many people complained about the peculiar and apparently absurd conclusions deduced from the theory which seemed to contradict the commands of common sense. "Look at this wise guy," they said, "he wants to show how smart he is by making fools of us." In fact, Einstein had not the least intention to extol his own smartness, rather he had the astonishing higher wisdom which comes to light in the structure of the physical world. In deep humility he mirrored in his speculations the cosmic spirit which manifests itself in all phases of physical events. The penetrating insight into the inner structure of the universe was the aim and the reward of this unique genius. Thus it happened that something that appeared as a loss in the beginning turned into a blessing when the full implications of the new world picture were properly understood.

This probing into the depths was something new in the annals of science. It never happened before that the relentless pursuit of one single idea—the relativity of reference systems—led to such sweeping results. In fact, it is to be wondered how man with the limited tools at his disposal can even claim to penetrate beyond the "veil of Maya," the deception of the external appearance. There was a time in the history of mankind when it was considered blasphemy to make any kind of inquiry into the working of the natural law. God made the universe in his infinite wisdom and it is not up to us to question his work. Any kind of experimentation with physical instruments was discouraged and looked upon with suspicion. Roger Bacon, the English monk of the thirteenth century, the excellent physicist who discovered the fundamental laws of optics by his ingenious physical experiments, was suspected of black magic and of being a disciple of the devil. He spent years of his life in prison and would have been burnt at the stake had he not had the good fortune to enjoy the protection of a few powerful friends among the higher clergy. Man has no right to question the handiwork of God. He should accept it in all humility and discard any second thoughts about it.

But the inquisitive mind of man could not be put to sleep. The dogmatic narrowness of a misunderstood religion gradually slackened and the time came when the scientific mind emancipated itself completely from the clutches of theological thinking. Now a new era began in which the emphasis was on experimentation. The theoretical approach came to be discredited because of the exaggerated emphasis of Aristotelian ideas during the Middle Ages, a period during which people frequently misunderstood the true intentions of this great philosopher who was also a great scientist. Now the pendulum swung too far in the opposite direction. The human mind became enslaved to the purely empirical and looked askance at Plato's world of ideas which tried to salvage the eternal substance from the fleeting world of sense impressions.

And now suddenly a man appeared on the platform who restored the equilibrium. He was a scientist of the highest order and nobody could suspect him of any kind of alchemistic tendencies. And yet he saw science in a new light. To him science did not mean the primacy of the experiment or the primacy of the theory, but the primacy of a deep reverence for the all-embracing lawfulness which manifests itself in the universe. He was more a visionary filled with rapturous admiration for the majesty of creation than a sober scientist. "The most incomprehensible thing about the world is that it is comprehensible," he said.

> Marvellous are thy works: and that my soul knoweth right well.
>
> How precious are thy thoughts unto me, O God! How great is the sum of them.
>
> If I should count them, they are more in number than the sand: when I awake, I am still with thee.

Such words, spoken by the Psalmist, would sound strange in a scientific treatise. But reading Einstein's papers we feel that here is a scientist who is imbued with the prophetic spirit, and that the Psalmist merely stated his ideas in poetic language.

This was religion as much as science. This was poetry and music and philosophy as much as science. No wonder that some of Einstein's greatest contemporaries from entirely different walks of life were attracted to this new way of integrated thinking. The great Irish dramatist and social philosopher G. B. Shaw had a strong predilection for the cosmic way of thinking and a great admiration for Einstein, whom he hailed as the greatest mind of the century (next to himself). Einstein came to London in 1930 and, associated with some charity drive, a banquet was given in his honor in the Hotel Savoy, to which H. G. Wells and G. B. Shaw were also invited. Shaw usually improvised his speeches. But this occasion he fortunately considered so important that he prepared his address in advance, dictating it to his secretary,

Miss Patch,* else this splendid toast would have been lost to posterity. He started out by comparing the two fundamental activities of the human intellect, Religion and Science:

> Religion is always right. Religion solves every problem and thereby abolishes problems from the Universe. Religion gives us certainty, stability, peace and the absolute. It protects us against progress which we all dread. Science is the very opposite. Science is always wrong. It never solves a problem without raising ten more problems.

In order to prove his thesis, G. B. S. now conjured up a wonderful scheme. In his opinion there were only eight great men of science, all the others were only tinkers who chiselled away on the ideas of the eight great leaders. (How he came to the number eight and according to what scheme he chose his eight great men of science is a secret that probably not even G. B. Shaw would have been able to tell.) These eight great prophets of science are: Pythagoras, Aristotle, Ptolemy, Copernicus, Galileo, Kepler, Newton, and Einstein. But even among these great natural philosophers there were only three who built complete universes—Ptolemy, Newton, and Einstein. And now G. B. S. continued as follows:

> Copernicus proved that Ptolemy was wrong. Kepler proved that Copernicus was wrong. Galileo proved that Aristotle was wrong. But at that point the sequence broke down, because science then came up for the first time against that incalculable natural phenomenon, an Englishman. As an Englishman, Newton was able to combine prodigious mental faculty with credulities and delusions that would disgrace a rabbit. As an Englishman, he postulated a rectilinear universe because the English always used the word "square" to denote honesty, truthfulness, in short: rectitude. Newton knew that the universe consisted of bodies in motion, and that none of them moved in straight lines, nor ever could.

* B. Patch, *Thirty Years with G.B.S.* (V. Gollancz, London, 1951), pp. 193–94.

But an Englishman was not daunted by facts. To explain why all the lines in his rectilinear universe were bent, he invented a force called gravitation and thus erected a complete British universe and established it as a religion which was devoutly believed in for 300 years. The book of this Newtonian religion was not that oriental magic thing, the Bible. It was that British and matter-of-fact thing, a Bradshaw.† It gives the stations of all the heavenly bodies, their distances, the rates at which they are travelling, and the hour at which they reach eclipsing points or crash into the earth like Sirius. Every item is precise, ascertained, absolute and English.

Three hundred years after its establishment a young professor rises calmly in the middle of Europe and says to our astronomers: "Gentlemen: if you will observe the next eclipse of the sun carefully, you will be able to explain what is wrong with the perihelion of Mercury." The civilized Newtonian world replies that, if the dreadful thing is true, if the eclipse makes good the blasphemy, the next thing the young professor will do is to question the existence of gravitation. The young professor smiles and says that gravitation is a very useful hypothesis and gives fairly close results in most cases, but that personally he can do without it. He is asked to explain how, if there is no gravitation, the heavenly bodies do not move in straight lines and run clear out of the universe. He replies that no explanation is needed because the universe is not rectilinear and exclusively British; it is curvilinear. The Newtonian universe thereupon drops dead and is supplanted by an Einsteinian universe. Einstein has not challenged the facts of science but the axioms of science, and science has surrendered to the challenge."

After this magnificent caricature which no one but Shaw could have drawn with such charm and boldness, he concluded:

In London great men are six-a-penny and are a very mixed lot. When we drink their health and make speeches about

† A Bradshaw is a British railway timetable.

them, we have to be guilty of scandalous suppressions and disgraceful hypocrisies. Suppose I had to rise to propose a toast to Napoleon. The one thing which I should not possibly be able to say would be perhaps the most important—that it would have been better for the human race if he had never been born. Tonight, at least, we have no need to be guilty of suppression. There are great men who are great among small men. There are great men who are great among great men, and that is the sort of man that we are honoring tonight. Napoleon and other great men of his type were makers of Empire. But there is an order of man who gets beyond that. They are makers of universes and as makers of universes their hands are unstained by the blood of any human being.

Needless to say, the mischievous remarks about Newton were in no way backed by Einstein who always had the highest respect for his predecessors and held Newton particularly in greatest esteem. In Newton's own time his theory of gravitation was a scientific deed of the first magnitude, particularly since Newton had to create also the mathematical tools of his discovery which did not exist before his time. His merits are by no means diminished by the fact that two hundred years later another genius came along who recognized the deeper implications of the Newtonian theory.

But what happened after 1925, when Einstein had still thirty years of his life ahead of him and his intellectual powers were still in full bloom? It was around that time that Einstein voluntarily abdicated from his role as the leading physicist of his generation and went into hiding. Many of his colleagues regretted this voluntary exile and felt that for many years to come Einstein could still have given great impetus to the new evolution which took place around that time. And yet, if we are aware of all the circumstances, we can only admire the intellectual honesty which prompted Einstein to withdraw and continue his speculations in the stillness of his study-room, undisturbed by the gathering clouds which increasingly obscured the vistas.

A new generation of physicists was on the march which threw

some of the most ingrained ideas of our customary physical think-ing to the winds. But why should Einstein resent that when he himself introduced so many new revolutionary concepts and dem-onstrated the falsity of so many commonly accepted ideas? Here, however, something was on the march that he was unable to accept. In all his strivings he was driven by the philosophical desire to understand. His general relativity brought this desire to full fruition. In this he could demonstrate to what unex-pectedly great results a philosophically oriented speculation can ascend if it is driven by a central idea which demands clarifica-tion. The new quantum theory was of a different kind, involving the manipulation of concepts whose philosophical meaning re-mained obscure. To assume that everything in nature is only statistical, that all our predictions in physics can only be based on the law of large numbers because the elementary processes of nature are governed by nothing but chance, was something that he could not reconcile with his own way of thinking. "The Lord does not throw dice" was the way he expressed it. From time to time he came out from his isolation and raised his voice in favor of that strict determinism without which he could not envisage rational science. But in every case he was the loser and soon he realized that he and his antagonists spoke two fundamentally different languages. Thus he gave up any further bickering, with-out modifying his own unalterable convictions.

The tremendous horizontal expansion of scientific knowledge frightened him more than it filled him with confidence. "Who would have thought around 1900," he wrote in a letter, "that in fifty years time we will know so much more and understand so much less"—a typical Einstein saying. The same letter contains another characteristic utterance: "Nowadays one can be happy if one is not trampled down by the stampede of the buffalos." It was clear that in a world in which science became a corporate endeavor and teamwork took the place of the flights of the lonely genius, an Einstein could no longer strive. He continued in prac-tically complete isolation to work on the great project which fascinated his mind ever since the success of his gravitational theory of 1916: the "unified field theory." If geometry is the great sink which swallows more and more of physics, why should we come to an end with gravitation? Perhaps, if we look very closely, we will find a place for electricity and maybe even the quantum phenomena. In fact, what else could be assumed, believing in the fundamental one-ness of nature?

But the old days of delirious victories did not return. There was no central idea which guided him through the dark with hypnotic power, as of old. Again and again he came up with possible solutions, but they did not have the convincing power of his earlier work. Riemann's geometry was somehow antagonistic to the type of symmetry structure which seemed to characterize the electromagnetic field. Shall we then shelve this geometry in favor of something still more general? But a generalization which is not carried by inner necessity is fraught with dangers. The geometry of Riemann was so natural and so self-consistent that no inherently valid motivation for its abandonment could be found, except the desire to go beyond the gravitational phenomena. The formal structure of equations now took the place of that marvelous physical intuition that characterized Einstein's earlier work. Here are Maxwell's equations, let us find some geometrical scheme which will lead to their interpretation. Such schemes could be found but they did not lead to anything fruitful.

The addition of a fifth dimension, the enrichment of Riemannian geometry by absolute parallelism, the change from metrical geometry to projective geometry—these are some of the schemes which were tried and abandoned again. Some relativists suggested another generalization in which even the existence of a line element is sacrificed in favor of an "affine geometry" in which forty, or even more formidably sixty-four, quantities took the place of the ten components of the metrical tensor of Riemann— a tremendous formal complication for which no physical justification could be found. Einstein experimented for a while with this idea but found it too brittle and hopelessly out of touch with physical reality.

Finally, during the last years of his life, he settled on the theory of the "nonsymmetric line element," in which the metrical tensor is retained but its symmetry abandoned, which means that instead of ten we have sixteen fundamental quantities. But then the geometrical significance of the theory is sacrificed and a formal edifice erected whose inherent necessity cannot be perceived. The mathematical complexity of this theory is such that we can take refuge in the hope that new results will follow after the mathematical difficulties are out of the way. Yet we have little reason to assume that this theory will solve the outstanding problems of physics, particularly the existence of atomism and the structure of elementary particles which became such a burning problem in the physics of our day.

In the meantime "modern physics" continues to grow and advance without taking account of Einstein's unifying attempts and, in fact, denying even the possibility of such an attempt being successful. Science is not out for the ultimates but continues to play the game along the well-beaten path of positivism, which denies all transcendental yearning toward the ultimates and confines itself to the "description and prediction of experimental results." But how refreshing to know that in our sober and drab times there lived a man who was full of inspiration and reverence for the magnificence of creation, who dared to speculate and produce marvelous results. How poor would our physical world picture be if this man had not broken away from the sober confines of contemporary science and erected a new edifice, singing in the wilderness and with laurel in his hair.

We have come to the close of this discussion of the place of Albert Einstein in the history of physics. It is not within the bounds of our subject to talk about Einstein as a human personality. And yet it is difficult to take leave of this great man without mentioning the extraordinary human qualities which singled him out among other great men of science to the same extent as did his scientific achievements. He was a man of destiny and he lived out his life as a man of destiny. He was fully aware of the extraordinary pedestal to which his unique mental faculties raised him, and this knowledge filled him with humbleness and humility. In a historical era of the greatest aberrations of human nature and the most absurd barbaric outburst which has ever swept the world, he did not despair of the ultimate victory of sanity and the old-testamental principles of justice and mercy. He did not retire into the cloistered silence of the scientific study, but raised his voice vigorously again and again against injustice and the suppression of individual liberties, unmindful of the most outrageous slanders to which he thus exposed himself and of the audacity of his adversaries who tried to identify him with the camp of the liars and murderers. With singular consistency he recognized the danger of annihilation of the human race caused by the blind nationalism which separates the people of the world and the unholy armament race to which they are driven. He saw the establishment of a world court and a world government as the only possible solution of the outstanding issues—tragically out of date in a world which recognizes the principle of "might is right" as the only practical basis of world politics.

In taking leave I could hardly do so more adequately than by quoting the inspired words in which the Protestant theologian Schleiermacher praised the memory of Spinoza, the great Dutch philosopher of the seventeenth century, who shows so many analogies to Einstein and whose cosmic philosophy was so near to Einstein's heart—words which equally apply to Einstein himself.

Him pervaded the Cosmic Spirit, the Infinity was his beginning and his end, the Universe his only and everlasting love. In holy innocence and deep humility he beheld himself mirrored in the eternal world, and perceived how himself was its most amiable mirror. Full of religion was he and full of Holy Spirit. Wherefore he stands there, alone and unequalled, a master of his art, but sublime above the profane rabble, a peerless beacon forever.

Bibliography

RECOMMENDED FOR ADDITIONAL READING

A. D'Abro: *The evolution of scientific thought from Newton to Einstein.* (Dover Publications, New York, 1950.)

Max Born: *Einstein's theory of relativity.* (Dover Publications, New York, 1962.)

A. Einstein and L. Infeld: *The evolution of physics.* (Simon and Schuster, New York, 1938.)

BIOGRAPHICAL

Philip Frank: *Albert Einstein; his life and times.* (J. Cape, London, 1948.)
Leopold Infeld: *Albert Einstein.* (Scribner's, New York, 1950.)
Carl Seelig: *Albert Einstein.* (Staples Press, London, 1956.)
Antonina Vallentin: *The drama of Albert Einstein.* (Doubleday, New York, 1954.)

ESSAYS BY EINSTEIN HIMSELF

The world as I see it. (Covici-Friede, New York, 1934.)
Out of my later years. (Philosophical Library, New York, 1950.)
Ideas and opinions. (Crown Publishers, New York, 1954.)

Epilogue

IN THE FOREGOING PAGES we have studied the revolutionary ideas of Einstein concerning the fundamental categories of the physical world: space, time, and matter. Yet we could hardly take leave of our subject without touching on Einstein's fundamental contributions to other fields of physics which, even if on the surface they do not seem to touch the deepest chords of physical existence, are not less characteristic of his extraordinary genius and which had in fact an even more profound influence on the development of contemporary physics than his relativistic speculations. These include his investigations concerning the nature of radiation, which had the most intimate relation to the development of a branch of physics called quantum theory.

That he could accomplish so much in this problem is due to his uncanny facility for being at home in all matters pertaining to statistics and probability. Many paragons of modern physics consider it a peculiar historical paradox that exactly the pioneer of the new statistical thinking, who had such a prodigious ability in the field of probability, should have separated himself from his colleagues by rejecting the probabilistic interpretation of physical laws, which seems to follow so naturally from his own discoveries. Indeed, if we could imagine the Einstein of 1905 suddenly transplanted to 1925, such a conclusion might have been justified. But in these 20 years much had happened in the life of Einstein and there was particularly the year 1915 in which his great masterpiece, the theory of general relativity, came to its triumphant conclusion. After this dazzling experience there was no return and his future course was uniquely designated. A return to his earlier pragmatic trend was no longer thinkable. As Einstein himself said once to a friend: "If someone had the good fortune to have found something essential, his life afterward can never be the same again."

"Heat" is a very common sensation, in fact the most important sensation from the standpoint of maintaining life. From the standpoint of physics it is a very peculiar phenomenon which forms a category of its own. The proper explanation of heat phenomena came only around the beginning of the nineteenth century when the idea took increasingly sharp contours that heat is caused by the agitated motion of billions of invisibly small particles (later called "molecules," which again are formed out of "atoms"), which form the material substance of a body. The conclusion was entirely inferential since in those days the validity of the atomic hypothesis could not be demonstrated by any palpable evidence.

The old idea that heat is caused by the agitated motion of material particles received more concrete shape in the work of Clausius, who was one of the first physicists to advocate a theory of heat which was entirely based on the motional energy of particles. In particular, he envisaged that the molecules of a gas were in rapid motion and that the pressure of the gas was caused by the very large number of impacts which were conveyed on the walls of the containing vessel by the impinging molecules. As to the velocity of these molecules Clausius made the simple assumption that they are all *equal* to each other, and the velocity increases with the temperature.

The first major breakthrough in the kinetic theory of heat was made by the English physicist J. C. Maxwell (Theory of Heat, 1871), who made a very fundamental discovery. It is astonishing that in spite of knowing practically nothing about the mutual action of the unobservable molecules, we can make very definite statements concerning the velocities with which they must move, by applying to this problem the laws of *statistics*. Two things help us in this endeavor. The one is that the molecules of a gas are physically all equal to each other (except for their position and velocities), the other that their number is enormously large. Maxwell was able to show that there is one very definite distribution of velocities, which has the property that the collision between the molecules will not alter it. Furthermore, if in the beginning this distribution, called the "Maxwell distribution," is by no means realized, the collision between the molecules will very quickly establish it and it will not change afterward.

The German physicist L. Boltzmann (Theory of Gases, 1895–98) extended and generalized the work of Maxwell and clarified the underlying structure by adding the inner and outer forces which may act on the molecules. Hence we speak of the "Maxwell-Boltzmann distribution law." Boltzmann met heavy opposition on the part of the leading physicists of his day, in spite of the fact that the kinetic theory of gases could explain a number of previously mystifying physical phenomena. The whole idea of the molecular hypothesis appeared as a plain hoax to a generation of physicists, who saw in theoretical constructions a kind of metaphysical element seeping into the solid structure of observational physics. (We must not forget that in those days no palpable evidence could be given for the existence of atoms and molecules, while the concept of "energy" seemed to provide a universal basis for the explanation of the totality of physical phenomena. The atomic hypothesis did not fit well into this "energistic" picture.)

In his student days Einstein read Boltzmann's treatise on gases with greatest interest and was extraordinarily stimulated by it. Immediately after finishing his university studies he began publishing his statistical investigations, in which he put the methods of Boltzmann into a broader framework. He was not aware of the important discoveries of the American physicist J. W. Gibbs, who somewhat earlier had anticipated Einstein's results and approached the problem from a still more fundamental viewpoint. However, in contradistinction to Gibbs, Einstein saw at once the possibility of applying the results obtained to definite physical situations. In particular, he discovered a very definite phenomenon by which the soundness of the molecular hypothesis could be directly demonstrated. He considered an emulsion, that is, a suspension of particles in a fluid (such as milk, for example).

These particles, although very small in themselves, are large compared to the size of the molecules of the fluid and in fact they are large enough to be directly observable under a microscope. Now Einstein demonstrated that these particles must perform a peculiar zig-zag motion, in consequence of the pushes of the many molecules which surround each particle and collide with it, because of the heat motion of these molecules. The power of statistics is so great that definite statements can be made concerning the magnitude of this zig-zag motion if one observes the path of such a suspended particle for a certain time. This was the celebrated 1905 paper of Einstein on Brownian motion. The observations fully corroborated the theoretical predictions and henceforth the molecular (atomic) hypothesis could no longer be seriously challenged.

But Einstein's statistical studies had a further consequence which became of fundamental significance for the future of theoretical physics. The heat radiation of a solid body represents a statistical problem. Here we have a tremendous number of molecules which are not merely interacting with each other but also with the electromagnetic radiation field which is present in consequence of the heat motion of the molecules. It seemed reasonable to apply to this problem the same principles by which Maxwell arrived at his distribution law. But then the vexing puzzle arose that the distribution of radiation energy derived from these considerations was in sharp disagreement with the actual observations; in fact, something seemed to go inherently wrong with the theory because it led to the peculiar conclusion that the total irradiated energy goes to infinity. It was Max Planck who in 1900 arrived at a distribution law which showed itself in perfect agreement with the observations. Planck endeavored to deviate from commonly accepted concepts as little as possible. He found that the proper radiation law is arrived at by assuming that the emission of energy of the radiating body does not occur continuously, but in definite "energy packets" of finite size, which he called "quanta." The word survived in the expression "quantum theory," which in its later development deviated sharply from the original course attempted by Planck himself.

Einstein's statistical insight went far beyond that of Planck. He pointed out the basic weakness of Planck's deduction and arrived at a much more radical conclusion concerning the nature of electromagnetic radiation. (On the human plane the conservative Planck and the radical Einstein were on very close terms and had the greatest respect for each other's scientific achievements.) With characteristic ingenuity Einstein inverted the process and posed the problem in the following form: "Instead of trying to deduce Planck's radiation law from some theoretical assumptions, let us assume the law and see, what kind of statistics is hidden behind it." What he found was amazing. The statistics hidden in Planck's law indicated that light does not behave like a wave which spreads out in every direction, but must be pictured as a bundle of energy which stays together and propagates with light velocity in a certain direction, exactly as if it were a *particle*, endowed with a definite amount of energy and momentum. He called this property of light "needle radiation" and used the word "light quantum" for the description of the corpuscular aspect of radiation (later displaced by the word "photon").

Einstein was so sure of the inevitableness of this argument that he claimed that Planck himself unknowingly introduced the light quantum hypothesis into physics, by the discovery of his radiation law. (How little Planck himself accepted this view is shown by his apologetic remark concerning Einstein's light quantum hypothesis on the occasion of his petition to the Prussian Government in behalf of Einstein, which resulted in Einstein's election to the directorship of the Physics Institute of the Prussian Academy of Sciences. After eulogizing the extraordinary merits of the candidate, he continues thus: "If in some of his speculations,—as for example in his hypothesis of the light quanta,—he was overshooting the target, this should hardly be counted against him. Without taking certain risks one would not be able to advance even in the most exact of the sciences." * The later development of quantum theory fully endorsed Einstein's revolutionary conclusion.) A few years later, in 1909, he

* Cf. Carl Seelig: *Albert Einstein* (Europa Verlag, Zürich, 1954), pp. 174–75 (author's translation).

went still further and applied his earlier method in evaluating the Brownian motion of a particle suspended in a fluid to the problem of the Brownian motion of a light mirror suspended in a radiation field. He showed that the statistical temperature fluctuations of this mirror around its average position are much larger than would be obtainable from the wave theory of light and are only explainable by assuming the corpuscular nature of light.

In the following years Bohr's atomic model revolutionized our physical concepts concerning the structure of elementary atomic processes. Einstein was eagerly interested in the new avenues thus opened to quantum theoretical speculations. In 1917 he succeeded with a new derivation of Planck's radiation law. In this investigation he gave a detailed picture of what happens to the atoms when they emit or absorb radiation. He considers a very large assembly of such atoms and assumes that a definite "transition probability" exists that an atom in an excited state will fall back to its natural (stationary) state. There is equally a definite probability that an atom in its natural state will be raised to an excited state. This is caused by the presence of a radiation field and is proportional to the intensity of that field with respect to that particular frequency. We should now think that perhaps the equilibrium between these two probabilities will yield the desired radiation law. This, however, is not the case. We have to assume an added action of the radiation field. The falling back of the atoms from the excited state to the ground state occurs spontaneously and can thus be called "spontaneous emission." In addition to this "spontaneous emission" there exists an "induced emission," again caused by the presence of the radiation field. Einstein assumes that the probability of the induced emission (falling back of the excited atoms to the ground state under emission of energy) and the probability of absorption (raising of the atoms from the ground state to the excited state under absorption of energy) are exactly *equal* to each other. The remarkable fact holds that these very general assumptions concerning the mechanism of radiation are sufficient to deduce Planck's radiation law, without further assumptions. This investigation of Einstein is one of the most ingenious theoretical contributions to the knowledge of nature in the entire history of physics. Here again it was of crucial importance that radiation be treated in a corpuscular way, in harmony with the light quantum hypothesis. The emission and absorption occurs as if very definite localized energies and impacts were at work, and not extended waves which do not allow that symmetry of emission and absorption that Einstein postulated.

A somewhat different approach for the derivation of Planck's radiation law was discovered by the Indian physicist S. N. Bose, whose paper Einstein translated into German. Here the statistical procedure itself is modified by assuming that the photons (light quanta) are indistinguishable from each other and thus should not be counted separately in their statistical action. Einstein immediately added to this derivation of Planck's law a further application by arguing that the same procedure should be applicable to the statistics of a monatomic gas. This leads at very low temperatures to a deviation from the ordinary gas laws which received the name "gas degeneracy." Einstein thus foreshadowed the idea of particles and waves behaving statistically similarly, with the consequence that we can expect that just as waves have in some respects particle characteristics, also particles have in some respects wave characteristics. It is thus understandable that Einstein hailed the French physicist de Broglie's discovery of the "matter waves" (1924) as a major discovery of physics.

Hence it is strange that in the later development of quantum theory, called "wave mechanics," Einstein no longer took an active part. He had the greatest appreciation and admiration for the results achieved, but he felt that the time had come for him to abdicate the leading role he had played previously as the foremost physicist of his epoch. A new generation of physicists grew up who payed lip service to his great achievements but in whose midst he felt as a stranger. Thus he separated himself more and more from the contemporary problems of physics and took refuge in his speculations aimed at a grand unification of all physical events in a final scheme, in which the apparent discrepancy between field events (continuous events) and quantum events would disappear. The radical new school of modern physics, which rejected causality and considered all laws of nature as of only statistical validity, was distasteful to him, the great master of statistical thinking. He did not deny for a moment the importance of statistical thinking nor the splendid achievements of the new quantum theory. But he could not reconcile himself to the idea that statistics should be the *final* word. He was convinced that the description of an electron (or of any other elementary particle) as endowed with mass, position, and velocity is a very naive picture, behind which lurks a highly complicated field structure which must be explored. If we knew this structure, the apparent whimsicality of the elementary process would disappear and the strict causality of all natural events be restored. But his high hopes of finding this structure did not materialize, whereas for his contemporaries the whole problem was no longer of interest, since they did not believe in the type of mathematical structure that Einstein considered as the only logically plausible one.

The last time that Einstein took a stand in a quantum theoretical discussion was in 1935, in his paper, "Can quantum mechanical description of physical reality be considered complete?" (written in collaboration with B. Podolsky and N. Rosen). This paper did not contribute anything essentially new to our knowledge of the quantum phenomena but had as its aim to demonstrate that the present quantum theory cannot be considered as the final word in describing physical reality. Schroedinger's psi function cannot refer to the individual event but to a large ensemble of individual events. To assume that the psi function describes everything means that the individual event cannot be the subject of scientific description, since the individual event remains undetermined, because of the statistical character of nature's laws. And yet—so runs the argument—measurements can be made in the sense of quantum theory which, although in themselves leaving the individual event undetermined, allow *inferential* conclusion as to the definiteness of the individual event. Ingenious as this argument was, it failed to convince the followers of modern physics, and Niels Bohr demonstrated in a discussion of Einstein's objection that the standpoint of quantum theory is free of any inherent contradictions.

We have no reason to regret that Einstein stood aloof in the last part of his life and failed to participate in the youngest phase of theoretical physics. He enriched science with a galaxy of brilliant discoveries which will stand out for all times as the most amazing manifestations of the human intellect in its groping for the ultimate. If he is a stranger in the present phase of science, this neither adds nor subtracts from the tremendous place that Einstein occupies in the history of physics. It is not impossible that the words of the philosopher-poet Friedrich Nietzsche may hold for Einstein: "And only when you have all forgotten me, then will I return to you."

Index